that
was
then

# That Was Then

by
Helga Skogsbergh
*illustrated by*
Mary Mantel

Published by
COVENANT PRESS
Chicago

# Contents

# PREFACE

It is late. The fires burn low as I finish the last page of this book. The story which began, years ago, in the book *Comes the Day, Comes a Way* has reached its natural end. It is a story of courage. It tells of the Swedish pioneers who settled on the wild south shores of Lake Superior, halfway up the coast of northern Wisconsin.

The spot of ground on which one has stood while weaving his childhood dreams is forever dear to him. Now in the late evening of life I have revisited the old homestead and its landmarks, reading pages of remembrance, plucking endless beams of light which have served as springboards to the generation which came later. It is hoped that the reader will find the paths into the yesterdays which I have tried to re-open in my search for footprints. A new crop of thick growth has sprung up in the pathways once marked by heavy boots and wagon wheels. But something still lives on, pointing the way to the ones who seek the higher guidance. There are lofty whisperings for the ones who listen. One can hear God in the starry heavens, in the quiet withdrawal of the waves as well as in the vastness of the lake itself, which—when still —holds in its bosom the reflection of heaven. Here are callings which come from another world.

Though yesterday and its people are now silent, the heart recalls the rustic simplicity of their life, their courage in the midst of rugged circumstances, the sturdy fiber of their trust in God, and the forward look to the land beyond this brief span of earthly existence. These are the spiritual landmarks they left behind them.

And standing here on the old, familiar ground which is ever calling the spirit to heighten its outlook, one recalls—and cries out—the words of Deuteronomy 19, "Thou shalt not remove . . . the landmarks which they of old time have set."

HELGA SKOGSBERGH

Minneapolis, Minn.
September, 1969

that
was
then

Most of the Swedish words and phrases which are found in the text of *That Was Then* are self-explanatory or are translated following their first use. Those requiring definition are included in the glossary found on page 124.

# *1.* THE BIG SEA WATER

A south wind wandered across the countryside that
evening, and the waves of the Great Lake rolled
dreamily toward shore. A "northwester" would have
pounced upon the waters like wild horses in a race
for land, the swells breaking upon the beach in angry
surf. But the south wind was of a different mood. It
swept its hand slowly across the harp of waves in
minor arpeggios that spoke of joys and sorrows, life
and death.

The primeval rhythm ever repeats itself—waves
rising in a moment of wild joy and high hope as they

leap toward shore, their foams of laughter dissolving on the soft sea sands. But then the still, slow moment of withdrawal, notes sobbing in the twilight. Here is no light chatter. Tones of depth rise to the surface like those which emerge from the breast of a harp when the strings are struck by a master hand—bosom tones with fervor in their call.

To the woman standing on shore nothing could more vividly portray the yesterdays than that which was released in the wave-tones of that evening. She began reading page after page of remembrance with a new and deeper meaning. Set to the accompaniment of the waves were dramatic scenes which moved across the vast stage of waters in panoramic view. Through the eyes of childhood she once again saw large ships laden with lumber slowly warping into the dim distance, vast floats of logs towed by ambitious little vessels called tugs, an Indian campfire ablaze on the distant point, a woman standing knee-deep amid the billows drawing a pail of water for the coming day. Innumerable scenes from the yesteryears rose before her, so clear, so alive.

But most poignant was a certain seaside memory of her father standing beside her as they watched the little sailboats set off on their voyage across the blue, their white sails glistening in the morning sun. "That," he said, "is life at its best. White sails lifted, stretched out to the last wrinkle, and driven by the winds of God across the ocean of life." White sails. Could she ever forget that morning?

Suddenly, as if in joyful recognition of a friend long lost, the waves leaped forward to greet the woman as she neared the water's edge, and the sweet communication she had once known—before she

4

left these shores for her pilgrimage into life—began again.

The woman was not unschooled in the language of the Big Sea. She had talked with waves way back in shore-toddling days and had listened with wonder to their melodies of intricate counterpoint. She knew what power they possessed to charm as well as to oppress. She remembered the times in childhood when she had chosen to walk the lake shore home from town as dusk fell upon the day rather than the roadway through the deep forest. Whatever the mood of the Great Lake, she found companionship here, a security when darkness drew on and she walked alone. She had seen these billows roaring in anger. She had heard their shouts of triumph. There were intervals when fathomless mystery lay across its silent awe, when greatness covered the deep. How she had listened! From its immensity had come questions seeming to say "Who are you?" "Why are you here?" "Where are you going?"

"Where are you going?" How often she had heard this question when the waters lay in sheets of silence. Others had heard it too. Her brothers had heard it. All who listened well had heard it: "Where are you going?" Always they had left the shores in serious thought, with a sense of hunger for the unexplored. The Great Lake never lost its power to open windows into strange new worlds.

Drawing a deep breath, she looked behind her. The crimson tones of autumn were gone, and the trees stood bare against a November sky. The last warmth of summer had fled, and the days had become short. Evidence of fading and withdrawal was all around. In the thick dusk she could hear the unfailing rhythm

5

of oncoming night. Familiar nocturnes rose from the Big Slough, sounds that had always belonged to this vast expanse of boggy wasteland. An owl added his sad overtones to the other voices that sang of dead summers. And always the ceaseless receding and returning of the waves. Each had its own voice, its own message.

"Whisperings of departed days," sighed the woman as she seated herself on a driftwood log to listen. Here was late autumn with its lonely, age-enduring charm. She could no longer question the personality of November with its intimations of the November which had settled upon her own three score and ten years. She was now living on a certain kind of time, a time that is borrowed. Something within one goes back—back to the landmarks known and loved when life was in its April and its June. For she was the Ingrid who had lived on these shores from infancy. She had fallen asleep to its lullabies and awakened to its matins. Countless footprints had marked these ribbed sea sands, for she had been an infant member of that brave two-family band who, in the dawn of the 90's, had settled in the raw wilderness bordering this lake— this ocean, with its allure of mystery, its sweep of openness, its shoreline graced in tall, majestic forest.

It was here, two miles up along the bending coast, that they had come that autumn day—the Hansons and the Isaksons, full-blooded Swedes with faith and iron nerve. With little more than a Bible under their arms and a lantern in their hands they had set their faces toward the austere wilderness where the footprints of the red man had not yet been erased from the Gitche Gume sands. Indians! Ingrid could hear, even now, the frightening knock on the cabin door

6

and the coarse voice saying: "Indian want bread."

*Ja, ack, ack,* her pale-faced mother had sighed when the stranger had slipped into the forest east of them and her last loaf had been given away.

"Indian want bread." Bread! Ingrid knew how vital was the word. Even in her young years she had begun to recognize the universal cry of man. So long as earth lasts someone knocks on a door and cries for bread.

"Cast your bread upon the waters," her father had said as they had gathered around their frugal meal that evening, "and thou shalt find it after many days."

Ingrid had often heard her father quote these words from Ecclesiastes. It was the postlude to his bits of sacrificial offering to missions. "Cast thy bread upon the waters." Strange how many early impressions were linked to this great body of waters. As a child she had envisioned slice after slice of coarse dark bread floating like driftwood across its immensity, now dipping out of sight, then rising again on the crest of the waves. On and on toward other shores it floated. It had become a framed picture on the walls of memory. Bread on the waters—for China, Alaska, and other parts of a world with various hungers. Some day it would return.

*Ja,* that was long ago. But unlike the many footprints that had been washed away by the waves of the decades, this memory had written its message on the log of time—"Cast thy bread upon the waters . . ."

Where was that strange charm which belonged to the genesis of those homesteading days? She tried to put back into flesh the ones who had begun the shaping of this new world, who had pushed back the dark forest with their naked hands and determinedly dug their spades into the hard earth with

7

visions of crops and herds, green patches of creative
fields, and, above all, a home. *Ack,* the blessedness
of a home. A foothold at last. She saw them, these
Swedish immigrants in their patient strength and
simplicity, and caught the very tone of each voice.
She heard again the soundings that came with new
beginnings, and she remembered that before long
this new land had begun to mold the pioneer just as
surely as he had done the land.

Suddenly Ingrid was awakened out of her reveries
by the sound of a distant bell. Could it be the same
chimes she had heard in her early womanhood, vespers floating from the steeple of the little Lutheran
church at the upper end of town? The pure tones
floated to earth like snowflakes on a winter eve.
Strange what the sound of a bell will do. Something
long forgotten comes back to life.

As Ingrid listened to the evening vespers, she was
carried into the realms of another era—the middle
years between life's seeding time and harvest—the
busy years where the past and the hopes for the
future come together—the romantic years, the age
of struggle and testing, days that weave patterns for
later years to view with comfort or regret.

Scenes and incidents long set aside returned again
as the golden tones descended on the countryside.
It was a bell that called the village folk to prayer
when the labor of the week was ended. A bell that
once sang with tones of gladness on a June evening
when two lovers joined in wedlock. And, *ack,* it was a
bell that tolled that autumn day when a procession
moved in solemn contemplation toward the lonely
hill where man's earthly pilgrimage must end.

Suddenly Ingrid recalled the shuddering clangs

8

of warning that fell like bolts of thunder when forest fires rose in hissing walls around the countryside. It shook the air, it shook the people, it shook the future. If not arrested, there was but one course to pursue. The bell rang to prepare the people to set their faces toward the Great Lake. Here in its harbor a large scow and lumber boat lay waiting, should the need arise, to carry the homeless out to the safe breast of its waters. The Great Lake—a shelter in the time of fire.

Strange how the mind will forget, only to be suddenly awakened by the sound of a bell.

The late afternoon was led slowly away by the gentle dusk. Ingrid could see the old buildings in yonder village setting their features against the oncoming night. A familiar loneliness accompanied the close of day on these shores. But she knew that out of the dark came rare compensations. In the high chambers of the soul are windows that open skyward, commanding views that are hidden in the brightness of noonday light.

She cast a far-flung look across the dark waters. There it was—that intriguing golden thread of light which in childhood had so fascinated her young mind. In her innocency that chain of light could mean nothing less than heaven itself. How often she had heard the older folk speak of the land beyond the sea of death. They preached it, they sang it, they pre-lived it.

> *This world is not my homeland,*
> *In tents I pass my days;*
> *Toward yonder shore of glory*
> *With yearning eyes I gaze.*

9

Even now, as she sat by the seaside looking across the dark expanse to the gold-edged shore, she felt an exalted closeness to the eternal shores. One does not easily outgrow the old shell.

Why had she come here? Why had she been so irresistibly drawn to the Great Lake in her return to the homeland? Was it to have an appointment with the past or the present? Was it to light the lamps of memory, to recapture moments she had once tucked away but which the years had allowed to escape? She knew it was more than the revival of memory and emotion. She had come to search for some witness which the passage of time had brought. How could she find the larger purpose and meaning of the life she had seen come to birth on these shores? What had sprung from these humble fields of beginnings? What sheaves had been garnered? Could any good thing come from these shores?

Ingrid tried to envision that long-ago spring morning back in the earliest 90's when her parents bent their backs over their small, newly-tilled patch of ground and pressed the first kernel of corn into the virgin soil to wrestle its way from death to life, from life to growth, and from growth to harvest. She could hear her father's instructions: "We must plant at least four or five grains to the hill. One seed is not enough. Not all seeds come to harvest."

Ingrid recalled the old nursery rhyme:

> *One for the blackbird*
> *One for the crow*
> *One for the cutworm*
> *And one to grow.*

10

She had learned early that there were many enemies bent on hindering growth. Every settlement has its own saga of thwarted lives, lost years, and remorse. Yet, here and there, struggling through the dark soil of adversity, came blades of green with the promise of standing ripe in the yellowing harvest.

"And one to grow." Ingrid began to ponder. What forces are there here to contribute to man's growth? Has not God placed in his universe many influences to help man find his highest best? Not least are the sanctuaries and schools of learning placed in the natural world about them.

*Earth's crammed with heaven*
*And every common bush afire . . .*

Here was the Great Lake, this timeless landmark, illustrating, teaching, speaking a message of hope as well as one of judgment, its vastness opening channels into eternal realms. And always asking the listening soul on shore: "Where are you going?"

But there were other landmarks at whose feet she must sit once more, some shining tower of strength, some tender Bethel to view again through ripe November eyes.

Stillness had settled upon the moor, upon the little village now covered by night. Dots of lamplight pierced the dark like early stars in the deep fields of the sky—one here, one there. The beauty of evening comes through in strange ways.

Ingrid rose from her driftwood log beside the waves and set her feet toward the old Corduroy Road which led to town and to her abode. By now the little town had lost its contours, but over the forest

11

wall the tip of a rich, full moon appeared in time to light the tired world down the mystic road which leads to sleep.

## 2. LITTLE TOWN

The sun rose in a burst of gladness as Ingrid set out to re-explore her home town the next day. There was happiness in the air, for when November smiles, it is the most beautiful smile of the year. The hour was early. Window shades had not yet been lifted, and no spirals of smoke announced that sleep was over and coffee pots were perking pleasantly on the stoves. She had walked but a short distance along lower Main Street when she realized how the decades had stamped their mark on the buildings which had once stood so hopeful and promising in the morning of their history. A few stood untenanted and forlorn like grounded ships, the smell of death settled upon their aging frames and no garden plot or late flower to bless one's coming in or going out. Yet each house was a story of many chapters.

A short way up the street she came to the vacant square which had once been a pasture where a cow or two had spent the time of day. It was still a vacant square accommodating a little path which short-cutted through it from corner to corner. Ingrid's eyes fell on the old pine stump which even now beckoned to passersby. She seated herself, glad for an opportunity to absorb in full the quiet wonder of the morning. Though the town had grown old and revealed much of the ashes of a past glory, it throbbed with an atmosphere that drew a long, mounting sigh from her breast. How exalting was this quiet moment alone, in a place so opulent with memories. It seemed to hold a sustained eternal note. It was one of those interludes when the familiar is transformed by a hallowed light. It might not be the same an hour or so later when the wheels of the day began to turn. Here was peace, the kind of peace which only the early hour can give.

Far below, past the long-silent sawmill, lay the Great Lake in beautiful repose. This morning its message, too, was peace. By the Big Slough to the west a remnant of sea gulls fluttered over its brown grasses, chanting their sad farewells to the dying season. Here, also, was peace, the solemn peace that speaks of change, the quiet closing of a door, the opening of another.

And to the east—*ack*, to the east. There rose the hills toward which she had set her eyes when, in the serious moments of childhood, she had quoted Psalm 121: "I will lift up mine eyes unto the hills, from whence cometh my help." These were the hills over which the morning sun poured its hope and promise for the day ahead. Tucked away in the

14

hillocks had once stood the crude log huts of some of the early settlers, their windows glistening in the sunsets—Bachelor Talbot, the Clarks, Sofie Monson, Johanna, and others. Ingrid could almost see them wave from their balconies. The hills of home. How they shared their towering strength with those who took time to turn their faces eastward. How often she had heard her father say, "Set your eyes on the hills when you pray in the morning. It will strengthen your faith." Like the Great Lake, these hills were God's spokesmen, placed in His universe to help man grow toward higher ground.

Ingrid drew her eyes back from far distances and looked at the close-at-hand. Her eyes fell on the narrow trail, which had never lost its chart. How often, as a child, she had tramped this little path to shorten the distance to the country school house. A little path. She could almost see the footprints of the 90's carved in its sod. The strip of ground on which a child has at one time trodden is forever dear to him.

Little towns . . . . little paths . . . . footprints. For a time it seemed she could hear the thud of the frontier foot and feel the urge, the dream, the prayer which accompanied the pioneer's thrust into the untamed wilderness. She could hear the tramping out of a path, later to be widened by wagon wheels into a road and at last straightened into the dignity of a main street.

Thoughts, feelings, and remembrances took on dimension as she sat alone in the hush of the morning. O little town . . . she could feel the heartbeats of all who had walked these lanes—the exaltations and degradations, the hopes and despairs of men who

15

had chewed both the sweet and bitter herbs of life. She felt the leavening spirit of the one intent in his search and struggle for truth and righteousness. She could understand the one who in his harvest years looked on his barrenness and listened to the sad whispers of his own uncreated song. There were those on whom a vacuum had settled, who in their narrow existence neither cared to ask questions nor find life's answers. Spread out before her were volumes of tragedy and blessing. The story is an ancient one . . .

. . . *some seeds fell by the way side . . . some upon stony places . . . and some among thorns. But others fell into good ground, and brought forth fruit* . . .

"Little town, little town, you hold in your bosom the tale of the ages," she whispered.

By now columns of smoke were rising pleasantly from chimneys, and the fragrance of coffee seeped from the breakfast hour out into the open air. Ingrid must leave her meditations for a while, then continue her way up the main street of the little town.

Passing old homes that have stood their ground as long as you can remember holds innumerable feelings. A special atmosphere surrounds the scene. Ingrid was glad to see buildings which still had the breath of life in them—curtains in the windows, smoke rising from the chimney, even late marigolds extending a welcome to the chance arrival.

Halfway up the street she paused in front of the large white house which had so often impressed her in childhood. Here, too, was evidence of fading and withdrawal. The house was no longer white but was clothed in the lonely, weather-beaten gray which time applies. This was the home where the village

16

chieftain had once lived. Through the years he had been popularly—and usually affectionately—called by the initials of his first two names: T. N. Rarely, whether by friend or foe, was he called by any other name. He was a remarkably just man, not given to petty bickering. She remembered her father's admiration for this man. "What would have happened to this settlement if T. N. had not come?" he had asked. "Yes, sir, T. N. is a man high-born." It was he who set in motion the wheels of industry so that there would be bread for the early tiller of the soil while he waited for returns from his small clearings. Out of his vision came the logging industry which gave men work in the logging camps of the forest during the winter months. At the lower end of town a saw-mill was erected. *Ja,* the sawmill! With its long whistle at noon, and again at six o'clock in the evening, it announced to men in their fields the time of day. "Has the mill blown yet?" they would ask each other. *Ja, ack,* how good to have a sawmill.

Large floats of timber were once drawn into the mill pond, and each log marched in single file up the tram and into the big saw, where it was sliced into fragrant timber. Commerce moved busily on the Great Lake, and long scows loaded with lumber set off across the waters to various ports along the lake. Here was material for building cities.

*Ja,* those were days when the little settlement on the shores hummed the tune of progress. Men's voices cut the crisp winter air with warning cries of "timmm-berrr!" And forest giants fell to earth, reverberating like earthquakes. Lumber, slapped on lumber, boomed across the countryside and rose in towers of majesty along the lengthy pier. Timber!

17

Sawmill! Lumber! Scows and tugs! *Ja, ack.* There was greatness. Yet this was not a glamorous kind of success. Everyone worked long hours for frugal returns, but there was happiness in hard labor and wise use of the hard-earned dollar.

Ingrid remembered the childhood thrill when on a Sunday afternoon they were allowed to walk the full length of the pier with its castles of lumber towering on both sides. Here was enchantment for the taking.

*Ja,* T. N. had his goals. "When a man has no dreams, he is poor indeed," he would say. He knew the barren, dreamless outlook of the very poor—how poverty can be a darkness—and he sought ways to help and encourage them. Often it meant digging deep into his own pocket to meet the immediate need. "*Ja,* T. N. has a big heart," folks often commented.

But the great days came to an end, and the Paul Bunyan saga vanished from the little settlement on the shores. The mill became silent, and so did the forests and the logging camps. The large lumber boats, the scows, and the tugs seldom graced the Big Sea waters; the long pier stood bare, waves beating against its aged frame.

And the big white house up the street, now frail with age, holds but memories of the great tycoon— T. N.—whose life came to an end shortly after the close of the lumber era, as though he were content to part with a world that had ceased to be his own.

Thus ended the logging drama. But Ingrid knew that strength and character had gone out from the big white house halfway up the main street. Sons and daughters of the town, impressed by this man of faith and vision and with a sense of obligation to his fellow men, never forgot. They had seen greatness in action. As each set out on his own pilgrimage in life, he carried a vision that ennobled his own plan for the future. And halfway up the main street of the little town one corner will ever remain a significant spot of history.

Ingrid drew a deep sigh, the kind of sigh which comes with exalted remembering. "And some seeds fell on good ground and brought forth."

## 3. BUILDING AGAIN

Another November morning was well along when Ingrid set out to further explore the old home town. She chose a forsaken lane that spoke of far-off days before it became matted by wayside weeds and quack grass. Had time left no mark on this community but that of wear and decay? Ingrid wondered. In coming back to her home town, some days before, she had passed half-starved farmsteads, the stables sagging and covered with moss. She had seen homes standing silent, mystery and loneliness reflected in the bare windows and breathless chimneys. This day she must reach the upper edge of town where the swift highway spoke of the possible dawning of a new day.

She passed the old Swanson grocery on her way. *Ja, ack,* this was still standing and in use in spite of its age, holding a miscellaneous supply of groceries, confections, leather goods, and other things. In early school days Ingrid and her brother Anders had sometimes stopped at the water pump behind the store, dry with thirst after the long tramp to school. Here from the spout of the old pump they had swallowed handfuls of refreshing water, taking turns to maneuvering the long handle while the other drank. *Ack,* it was handy to have this modern convenience behind the store to refresh the thirsty wayfarer. *Ja,* that was then.

Presently Ingrid heard steps coming up the board walk behind her. They were slow, well-measured steps, with a note of contentment in each footbeat, as if the pedestrian knew his ground well and had no uncertainty about the way ahead.

Ingrid turned to see. Isak? Could it be Isakson's Isak? *Ja,* think, so it was.

"No, but see who is here, if it isn't Ingrid," he exclaimed in surprise. "When in the big world did you get to these parts?" Isak reached out a warm, gnarled hand to greet her. The Scandinavian in Isak's voice was still there. His roots had never been torn from this soil. Ingrid studied the features of the old man and saw that the years had written their many chapters. But it was not difficult to detect again the glint in the eye of the little neighbor lad with whom she had built sand villages on the shore in the days when life was a delightful, mysterious dream

21

and the world was full of every imaginable kind of magnificence. That was more than seventy years ago. What fun they had shared in their simple, toyless childhood, a childhood glowing with country-fed imagination.

"But, Isak, what are you doing in town so early in the day?"

"*Ja,* say that. I'm going to the Co-op store at the top of town to buy some grub before it closes down. It is going out of business soon, they tell me. I am batching it alone now. On the old homestead by the lake. The new owner wants me to stay on until he is ready to take over. And that's okay with me. Come with me, and I will show you a few changes that have happened since you were here last."

They had walked but a short distance when the scene gave way to some new unfoldings. Along the big state highway two periods of time seemed to meet—yesterday and today. Ingrid had seen the state roadway before. This morning it lay like a blue ribbon along the upper edge of town, heading eastward to other parts of the Wisconsin northland. Independent and swift ran the road above the village, stately and reserved. Already cars were speeding along with neither time nor awareness of the little seaport below. Only a rare motorist paused to behold the wonder and serenity reflected in the great water basin below.

"*Ja,* times have changed," commented Isak. "At least something of a new day streaks through our quiet community. Now they come like lightning. It's not like the day when our fathers rode along with horse and wagon, stopping here and there to talk to another settler plowing his acre by the side of the road. 'Stop in and have a cup of coffee,' the man behind the plow might well have said. And busy as they were, they would tie their horses to a fence post and spend a half hour sharing with each other the news of the little world they knew, talking too about their need of tools and farm machinery and the empty pocketbook. The cup of Arbuckle's coffee tasted good all right in the middle of the long forenoon, and if the visitor was your father, Ingrid, like as not he would leave a Bible verse before he untied his horse to go. 'Come to our prayer meeting next Thursday night,' he might have added. 'At Ernst Johnson's log house on Flag River road.' Then off he'd go, the wagon wheels squeaking in the sandy ruts. *Ja, ack*, there was time in those days. Now they go like lightning."

If what Isak saw was like lightning, what would he say if he saw the street in the big city where Ingrid lived? *Ja, ack*, the wheels of earth are ever increasing in momentum, spinning much too fast to see the symbols of eternity all around them—a sunset in the making, the upward look of a flower, the glory of the midnight star—and much too fast to have on hand a divine promise of comfort and direction for the perplexed one wondering what life is all about. Pushed from behind by the human stream and pulled by the green light up ahead, man misses the illumination of the high moments.

"Maybe we should take a little time off ourselves this morning," suggested Isak, pointing to the attractive little *stuga* at the place where two roads came together—Helga's Coffee Shop. "A cup of *elva kaffe* wouldn't taste so bad."

Ingrid was glad to follow Isak into the friendly

little inn, and after some nods and handshakes they were seated at a table facing the familiar world below—the little town, the Big Slough, and the Great Lake.

"Coffee for two?" the waitress asked, smiling at Isak.

"*Ja*, and I think we should have some of that Swedish coffee bread." Isak pointed to the newly-baked breads on the table across the room.

In the coffee-fragrant comfort of Helga's Cafe Ingrid felt she had moved into the 1960's again. The touch of a new day seemed to accent this little *kaffe stuga* along the side of the busy highway, and yet the atmosphere of the past was not missing. Ingrid swallowed a sip of coffee, then turned her gaze to the town below.

"But tell me, Isak, what has happened to this town. True, there is a big highway and a few new homes tucked away in the outskirts, a Co-op store, and always the impressive school house. But a peculiar sleep has settled over so much of the countryside. You remember the days when there were logging camps, mill whistles, and towers of lumber marching in long rows toward the sea. No more does one see the lumber boats, the passenger steamers, the scows, and the little black tugs. How one misses the life that was once in motion on that great body of water below. *Ja, ack*, that was yesterday. Now where do we go from here?" Ingrid drew another sip of coffee. "Where are the young people, the middle-aged generation? What has become of the town and some of the farms with their look of gathering age? And the empty church on the hill?"

"Oh, things will change," prophesied Isak. "We

24

will see a new day up ahead. Everything has its season. Important city people are nosing around these parts looking for land along the lake, like the fellows who bought our childhood homes—yours and mine."

Ingrid had yet to visit the old homestead on the shores which had changed hands three times since she and her brothers surrendered it. She would save this visit till later.

"Something lies up ahead," continued Isak. "You feel it coming. We will take a walk east of the old Catholic church, where you will find some new homes smiling through the trees, all dressed up in city fashion. It is just a little sign of what may come. Of course, our men have to find work in the city. Many have moved, families and all, but their plan is to come back when they are old enough to retire. They are holding on to their homes here and the patches of ground they own. They will be back, and the town and countryside will come to life again. You will see. Look what has happened to the old homesteads. The land along the lake which a few years back was sold for a few dollars an acre is now being sold in one-foot strips for a fancy price per foot. By the foot, mind you. When once the smell of the lake and the sound of the waves gets into your blood, you never really pull up roots." He spoke of the day when lights from every vacant house would dot the countryside, when modern comfort and convenience would grace the land and industry would be set in motion. Isak was never one to lose sight of new dawns. Ingrid recalled the calm reactions he showed in childhood when things went wrong. She remembered how hard they worked building sand villages on the beach only to find them washed away the next morning by the waves of night.

"Oh, we will build again," he would say, "a little higher up from the waves." Always there was a note of hope in his voice. And with renewed fervor and strong wings of imagination they planned and gathered and built again. Before long another sand village spread itself along the beach with towers, rivers, twig forests, homes, a church, a school—a world! How well they remembered this.

Like the village on the shore built by little children's hands but washed away by the billows of night, so this little town, too, had given way to the waves of time and circumstance.

"It is ever so with the things of earth," sighed Ingrid, "houses built on the sands."

For a long moment Isak and Ingrid sat in silence, thinking their own thoughts. The early forefathers— what kind of a building plan did they have in mind as in simple faith and painful sacrifice they plowed their first furrows in this wilderness soil? Theirs was not a vision of a coming Eden, clothed in the splendor of modern ease and devices. Little did they dream of the endless frontiers man up ahead would explore, of ventures into upward and outward space, of sky-searching thrusts toward distant planets and stars. Their concern was not for stately mansions and laying up for themselves treasures on earth. The vision to which they clung involved another kind of building, not on the sands of time but on the rock, something solid, imperishable, eternal. Earth was not their home. They were but pilgrims here. Their citizenship was in heaven. The hope they cherished

was expressed in the song they often sang: "We wait
for a great and glorious day."

> *O wonderful day that soon may be here!*
> *O beautiful hope the pilgrim to cheer!*
> *Thy coming we hail in tuneful accord,*
> *Thou glorious day of Christ, our Lord.*

These were the thoughts and remembrances that
came into expression as they visited together that
November morning in Helga's Coffee Shop—Ingrid
and Isak. In spite of the strength the years had
taken, the dimmed vision, the stooped frame, they
were building again—hopefully, seriously—another
village on the white shores of the Big Sea Waters.

# 4. THE LUTHERAN PARSONAGE

It was the last house on the left side of Main Street going south. Ingrid had reached the upper end of town and found it was still there, the old place that had been the home of the Lutheran minister and his family some sixty years ago.

Pastor Olson had possessed the distinguished mark of a real shepherd of his flock even to his white, flowing beard. They called him Prästa Olson. One block down the street stood the steepled church where each Sunday he fed his congregation the undiluted Word of God.

But the little manse had been more than a house at the upper end of town. It had served as a haven of light and shelter for many forms of shipwreck and frustration. Ingrid paused to set aside sixty-five years of her life and became a child of ten once more, holding a memory that could never be forgotten.

She remembered the story of the night the parsonage became flooded with light at two o'clock in the morning. Some weeks before a fellow settler, destitute and ill in body, soul, and mind, had found shelter in the home of the pastor and his kind wife. Guldstrand was the bachelor up along Flag River who in his early settling days had often expressed his joy in the Lord with his appealing song and guitar music. At the log cabin prayer meetings it was always, "Play a song for us, Guldstrand."

*Ja,* Guldstrand and his guitar—never one without the other. It was a scene on the screen of memory that Ingrid had always kept.

But a cloud had settled darkly on the sky of Guldstrand's soul. A door seemed to have closed between him and his heavenly Father. It is likely that the Lutheran pastor was the only one who knew what had really happened. Guldstrand lost his song. Then his health began to fail him, and he felt himself alone in a guilt-ridden world of his own.

Then it was that the parsonage door, like a long arm, had swung open. In its haven he was cared for, prayed for, and given the love he so desperately needed in his helplessness and lostness. Little by little through the ministry of prayer and counseling a great change came about. It is not given to all to open the reaches of another's heart. But Prästa Olson possessed this gift.

It happened on a cold winter night when slumber lay heavy over the white countryside. Heaven slipped into the parsonage, into the room where the sick man lay. The pastor was suddenly awakened by a song coming from the upper room. He hurried upstairs, and upon entering the room he knew that a miracle had taken place. Joy seemed to be flooding the entire room.

"I have found Him again," the man exclaimed, his eyes blurred with happy tears. "It feels so good here," he said, and he laid his hand on his breast. Forgiveness had entered the room in the home at the upper end of town.

In no time all the kerosene lamps were lit. "It is fitting," said the old pastor, "that all windows fling the golden light of the good news into the night. A soul has found peace with God."

Soon every member in the household was up, praising God for answered prayer.

There were many other scenes the little manse up the road held within its walls. Ingrid remembered the time back in childhood when her mother took to attending the Lutheran church. The Lutherans were the only religious body in the community who could afford a resident pastor. Ingrid's folks belonged to the humble few called Mission Friends, visited only on rare occasions by a preacher. The two denominations did not see eye to eye in their manner of worship. Each felt the other was on a questionable track, and a wide gap existed between the two. Here was no opportunity for ecumenicity.

"Much too cold and formal," said the Mission Friends of the Lutheran church. "Too sentimental and lacking in form," said the Lutherans of the other group.

Much to the alarm of her own people, Ingrid's mother, by some inexplicable compulsion, began attending the Sunday morning services in the Lutheran church. Perhaps, thought Ingrid, she had wanted to strike out on a crusade of independence and for a

31

few brief hours unshackle herself from the close confines of endless drudgery. Perhaps she had some other reason. She may have had a need no one else understood. She saw to it, however, that Sunday dinner was well under way before she left and that Ingrid was given instructions how to go about adding the final touch—"Just in case," she would say.

She was well received by the Lutherans and especially by Pastor Olson and his wife. Making new friends was a great achievement. She longed to enlarge her friendship world to include more than her neighbor Emma—good as it was to have Emma.

She was different when she returned from these services in the Lutheran church. There was beauty and gladness in her walk, and in the days that followed she lived with a new look on her face and a soft tone in her voice.

*Ja*, Ingrid's mother took off for the Lutheran church again and again. Her father, strangely, had not objected. One Sunday something happened. Who should invite her for dinner but the parson himself and his wife. Imagine! Dinner at the parsonage!

Ingrid recalled the new spring in her step when she came home that afternoon. There was a high look on her face and no words to describe her elation. She talked about it all week. To Emma she reviewed every word, every minute, of her visit.

"You should see how pleasant they have it. No milk pails or slop pails, Emma, and no cow smells around. And the china cups and silver coffee pot and all. Most of all you should have seen the kind way Mrs. Olson treated me, a poor country woman out of the woods."

Ingrid had felt that her mother's visit at the manse had changed the status of her whole family.

During Prästa Olson's ministry more people had settled in the community. The township was big enough now to boast of families with similar names, especially if the names were Johnson, or Olson, or Larson, and this sometimes caused problems. Ingrid well knew the Mrs. Olson who lived in the last house at the low corner where the town tipped sloughward and where lonely herons stretched their necks above the slough grasses. She had often knocked at Mrs. Lars Olson's door with a basket of butter. And just as often she had gone away with coins tied in one corner of her handkerchief as payment for the butter. Mrs. Olson liked Mama's butter. The pounds were large, fresh, and yellow. It was not she Ingrid thought of, however, that morning of mornings a few days after Mama's visit at the parsonage when she was awakened by the announcement that she was to get dressed and go to town with five pounds of butter for Mrs. Olson.

Thrilled at the thought, she took no end of pains in her dressing. In no time she was on her long trek to town. Even with the heavy basket of butter the hour seemed short. This was no ordinary undertaking. She rehearsed a number of words as she walked along, for she wanted to appear at her best when she reached her destination. Reaching town, she walked the full length of the only street and turned in at the last house to the left. Her heart beat fast. Imagine the excitement of entering the home where a minister lived! She climbed the steps and rapped on the front door of the parsonage. Mrs. Olson was there immediately to open it in the gracious manner that ministers' wives are trained to open doors. Ingrid recalled how she had hoped that some day she would be a minister's wife and open doors like that.

She remembered handing the basket over to Mrs. Olson. "I have brought you five pounds of butter from my mother," she stammered. Mrs. Olson lifted the white cloth and looked into the basket, her face both surprised and perplexed.

"Are you sure all this is for me?"

"Oh, yes, all of it, and there will be more later," she answered with breathless enthusiasm.

She followed Mrs. Olson into the kitchen, where with thoughtful concern she emptied the basket. What a pleasant kitchen it was. The ten o'clock sun streamed through the snow-white curtains, and the fragrance of coffee gave its usual note of warmth to the setting. A yellow bird sang from his cage above. In the other room Pastor Olson sat relaxed in his large leather chair reading a thick book; the big letters on the covers spelled "Martin Luther." When he saw Ingrid, he came out to greet her, and Ingrid, blushing, felt she was shaking hands with greatness itself.

"I don't know how to thank your mother for all that butter," said Mrs. Olson as she served Ingrid a plate of fresh cookies and a glass of milk. "I just wonder . . ." she said, leaving the sentence unfinished.

"Oh, that was nothing at all," answered Ingrid as she slipped her arm through the handle of the empty basket and got ready to leave. Mrs. Olson followed her to the door, and the farewell was as sweet as the greeting had been.

That noon Ingrid had walked home on air. She hadn't even stopped to look for the crow's nest in the Big Pine. She was swelling with happiness to share with her mother regarding her trip to the Olsons. She couldn't wait to tell Annie, her neighbor pal, of the stature she had reached that morning as a guest in the Lutheran pastor's home.

"You back so early?" her mother had asked as Ingrid came rushing in, out of breath. "I hope you didn't lose the money."

Money? Lose what money? What did her mother mean?

"I gave the butter to Mrs. Olson and told her you sent it. And she said thank you a thousand times, and that it was too much. I answered her that it was nothing at all."

Her mother looked disturbed. "I can't understand; Mrs. Lars Olson always pays me spot cash for my butter."

Mrs. *Lars* Olson! So it was Mrs. Lars Olson the butter was for! Why hadn't her mother made that clear? Ingrid explained how she had gone to the parsonage with the butter. After all, what name had been spoken more often in their home during the past weeks than that of Pastor Olson? Oh, what a mistake.

"You dreamer," Mother had called her. "You must go right back to the parsonage and explain what a mistake you have made and how sorry you are. Then you must ask for the butter and go right down to Mrs. Lars Olson with it."

Ingrid remembered her mother mumbling about the money she was counting on for immediate use and other words belonging to the vocabulary of the poor.

Ingrid could never forget that walk back to town, tears rolling from her cheeks and dropping into the sands of the road. If her mother had asked her to swim across the Great Lake, she wouldn't have felt the impossible any more. How she wished she could be transported to another decade and that this day could be lost in the annals of time. If it were only ten years from then, or even one year. How different she might feel on April 25, 1903. She knew, of course, how the whole town—and the children at school—would find out about this mistake. *Ja, ack.*

Oh, that this day were over, she sighed as she finally reached the door of the Lutheran parsonage.

But she did not need to knock. The kind minister's wife was at the door, as if she had stood there waiting for her ever since she left two hours ago. Ingrid was sure Mrs. Olson could see the tear-stained look on her flushed face, but she hoped she might understand the sensitivity of a ten-year-old who had blundered so shamefully. Whatever it was, Mrs. Olson had a way with her that immediately loosened the pent-up fears and embarrassments, and Ingrid remembered feeling that she had awakened from a horrible nightmare into the sweet atmosphere of security and understanding. She had stammered some words about her mistake, but Mrs. Olson brushed away everything with a soft laugh that had the feel of healing balm in it. Then she told Ingrid something that changed the whole day, the whole year, and many years. She told how she had been a ten-year-old girl back in Scandinavia and how the very same thing had happened to her. She had made the same kind of mistake. Ingrid had felt sure that the minister's wife wasn't making it up to comfort her. And yet her mistake had perhaps been somewhat different. It may not have been a basket of butter delivered at the wrong place. It could have been a basket of eggs, or of berries. Perhaps the minister's wife had been a little ahead of her time in her understanding of a child's hurt and frustration. Ingrid would always bless this memory because of her. She had found in this home what many older folks had found—the warm release that comes from understanding and a new courage to pick up life and go on.

She remembered carrying the five pounds of butter down to the corner of town where the Big Slough crept up close to Lars Olson's house. Her errand finally made right, and with the money tied up in one corner of her handkerchief, she started for home. It was a new person walking the long road back in silence, for she had grown that day—grown several inches taller—deep inside. *Ja*, that was then.

The white house in the upper end of town had many colorful tales stored within its breast. How many feet had climbed the steps to that front entrance. How many hands had knocked on its door. And always it had opened—warmly, readily—to all manner of ills, even to a ten-year-old child's mistake.

Ingrid was suddenly awakened from her long recess into the past and wondered how she could have lost herself so completely in the dramatic events that once took place within the walls of the little parsonage across the street. Twilight had begun to cloak the day, and she knew the November night would fall quickly. From her position across the street she drew one closing view of the old landmark and reluctantly walked away. Truly it had been a lighthouse shining through many shades of darkness.

# 5. THE COUNTRY ROAD

Many there are who travel the highways, ride the trains, or sail in ships. Others fly the skies. The distant corners of the earth may someday be but a moment's journey. Before long the highest star and the deepest sea may be within the reach of man. But to Ingrid there was no wayfaring quite as rich in meaningful discovery as traveling by foot the old-fashioned country road between her home and the little town. Though the old road lies forsaken now, it is a living landmark calling to its own. Since she had come back to refresh herself at the primal springs of her early life, she must tramp its sands once more.

"I may get no farther than the length of the

corduroy stretch," she told her brother, who offered to take her by car, "but I must at least try. There are treasures to recapture along that road, and I must do it alone."

It was a long two miles or more, the road between her old home and the little village. Ingrid doubted if the distance had ever been measured. It could have been three miles counting the Corduroy Road which lay across the sprawling slough.

The Corduroy Road—*ja*, who could ever forget it? It was the last stretch on the way to town. It had been laid with short cedar logs placed transversely like a long washboard across the Big Slough. She could recall the mysterious rattle of wagon wheels rolling over the cedar beams in the still of a summer night. It resounded over the countryside for miles.

Back in childhood, as winter deepened, the walk along this slough road provided all the discipline in patience and courage that a life would seem to need. Winter gales slapped the wide marsh with unrelenting force. Snowdrifts sometimes reached paralyzing depths. Willow bushes shrieked with pain. There was no choice for the struggling traveler but to set his face like a flint against the cut of the wind and go right on.

Going home from town, this difficult stretch came first. How indescribably comforting was the entrance to the calm shelter of the forest road—like casting anchor in a safe harbor after a terrifying storm. Here no wind could gain entrance, for the road was protected on both sides by tall walls of snow-peaked timberland—pine, spruce, balsam, and cedar. Soft whisperings in the treetops spoke of peace that follows tempests, of rewards at the end of struggle.

40

"*Ja,*" thought Ingrid, as she entered the forest sanctuary on this November day and sank her feet into the deep sands of the winding road, "*ja, ack,* here was life's contrast in bold illustration." As a child, how little she had realized what exercise in faith and courage was being drawn along this road for the years ahead. When the winds of adversity had come, when life's road had become blocked by drifts of trials and hardships, how helpful had been the memory of the Corduroy Road and the renewal of a hope that somewhere up ahead was the calm shelter of the forest road. Or if the journey headed townward, how likewise comforting the thought that at the upper end would be the village store with its open door and crackling wood fires beckoning old and young to draw up close. *Ja, ack,* hope must not die when you walk your Corduroy Road in the storm. What was it her father had said?

"Always keep an eye on the journey's end when you walk against the wind."

Strange what an impact a road can make on a young life.

She remembered when the town was prosperous enough to supply a school bus for the children living far from town. Built over the wagon, or sleigh, was an arched frame covered with canvas. A school rig, they called it. The Hanson and Isakson children were among those who were picked up. But the noise of many voices sometimes bothered Ingrid, and often on the way home from school, when time was more lenient, she chose to walk. It afforded opportunity to think, to imagine, to feel, to build dreams. How much goes on inside a person when you walk undisturbed along a friendly road walled in by a

41

spired forest and roofed over by a strip of blue heaven.

This old-fashioned roadway, once deeply rutted by wagon wheels, held a volume of memories for her. It wound its way through the forest in interesting curves, with no concern about length or time. Every turn held a history of scenes, sounds, voices, and awakenings of past sensations. Ingrid had sometimes heard her father tell of encountering, like Moses of old, a burning bush and finding God's nearness in a significant way. Many a door had been opened to the inner life, many horizons broadened. Here man found simple dialogue between the two voices within himself. This was not a complicated age of many voices. Along this road many an inner conflict had ended in fervent prayer as the wayfarer walked alone or paused at the foot of a towering pine. Many a tear had fallen into its sands. Here decisions had been made, plans constructed, ideas and dreams given birth, and the traveler had come to the end of the way wiser and nobler for time spent alone on the forest road.

Along this lane lovers had walked with sweet leisure, hand in hand, under the starry skyway. Accompanied by the soft notes of pine song, they had whispered in the tender language of romance their new-found love. Together they had dreamed of the enchanted world which lay before them. How suddenly wonderful life had become! *Ja, ack,* what chapters of romance a road holds. It is a landmark of many secrets.

But a road also has nooks of mystery. Ingrid recalled the little bridge as one neared the Isakson farm. It spanned a pond of water fed by a stream from the ever-present Big Slough. In the spring it quivered with life, and the chorus of frog song on an April evening gave to the world an unforgettable serenade. Ingrid and her companions loved to stand on the bridge and see themselves mirrored in the clear waters that gathered after the winter thaw.

She remembered the day when a man of Finnish birth, who had settled on the shores for a time, came upon the children.

"If you should fall into that pool of water, you would sink so deep you would reach the land of Finland," he told Ingrid and her playmates.

This caused no end of mystification to the young minds. There arose much questioning and pondering about the matter. The teasing chance remark, spoken by a stranger, grew in content and consternation until this dramatic spot along the road became labeled as "Finland" by old and young alike. "On the other side of Finland," they would say when referring to a location along the way. "Just a little on this side of Finland."

"*Ja, ack,*" thought Ingrid, as she stood on the little time-beaten bridge, "every road must hold some tale of mystery."

How often Ingrid had heard her mother refer to the solace she found in going to town.

"*Ja,* think how good it is to get away for a spell from this log house and the endless scolding and complaining of the waves on the shore," she would say as she filled her basket with prints of butter. "In the quiet of the woods I can drop my worries, empty my brains, and find myself again."

Along this road she and her neighbor Emma had deepened their friendship as they trudged to town with their baskets of eggs and butter. How often they had taken time to rest along the way on the friendly pine log which, years ago, had fallen by the wayside for just such a purpose as this. They had set their baskets in the nearby clumps of moss, drawn deep breaths of the fragrant forest ozone, and begun to talk, each minute drawing closer to the reaches of the other's heart. Moments like these provide a special occasion for confidences such as women need. There were burdens that only women understand. There was talk of necessities—the coat she desperately needed before the oncoming winter, the baby that would be coming in the spring, the husband she could not always understand, the log hut which was becoming increasingly smaller. And who should house the preacher who was to come some time in June? *Ja,* say that.

But the confidential sharings usually ended on a familiar note. Rising to resume their journey, the old philosophy expressed in a Swedish proverb capped the intimate roadside moment: "Comes the day, comes a way." A road through the deep woods is made for friendship.

It was on this road that Ingrid's brother Emil voiced his dreams to the heaven above as he walked alone talking to himself. Inspired by what he had learned in the country school about men of greatness—Washington, Lincoln, Jefferson, men who had lived and given—he had awakened to the fact that he, too, had a life to live and share. What should hinder him from adding his name to the list? Moved by high aspiration, he spelled out his dream in audible words, little realizing that behind the roadside bushes were his comrades, curious to hear what this queer playmate had to say.

Shifting his stack of books to his left side, the dreamer would use his right arm to add emphasis to his words:

"My father has decided that I shall be a preacher when I grow up. I shall not be a preacher. I shall be President of the United States like Lincoln and Washington was."

Little wonder that he was nick-named "President" by his teasing playmates. "Here comes the President, let us hear from him," they would call as he entered the playground of the school. But that did not seem to annoy him. He found happiness in his dream.

Ingrid's brother did not make the climb to the position of the nation's first man, but early in life he had hitched his wagon to a star. Struggling his way courageously through tunnels of poverty and hard work, he plowed his lonely furrow upward in the area of education from country school to high school, from teacher's college to several universities, until he attained the top degree in his chosen field. All because there had been a dream that nerved his brain and hands to action. Ingrid had seen his name listed that very year as one of the outstanding civic leaders of the day. There is no doubt that the old country road had helped provide the stimulus needed for a young lad's vision and upward reach.

Ingrid had tramped a pleasant stretch of the old road when she came to what had once been called The Long Path. There were shorter paths that branched off from the main road only to return again up ahead. Trails came into existence when the children began exploring curious treasures beyond the edges of the roadway. Pushing their way through brush and growth, they might come upon the rarest wild flowers in the spring: the trailing arbutus, various kinds of violets, jacks-in-the-pulpit. In the late summer the wilderness provided large patches of ripe blueberries and bushes of blackberries in sweet juiciness. On a winter morning curious little tracks made by the prowling creatures of the night told their soundless story. What fascination it had been to follow these footprints into the deep snows beyond the wayside. Little by little the forest gave way to snatches of trails which eventually tied together. With continued tramping, the ill-defined passageway soon became a footpath idling throughout the forest as carefree as a rabbit. An interesting story is the making of a path, mused Ingrid.

But The Long Path was a long one. "A path is supposed to shorten the journey and save time," said some of the old folks, "but not so with this one." In their concern about time they failed to discover the wonders which The Long Path had in store. It is ever thus, thought Ingrid.

She tried to break through the windfalls obstructing the entrance to the old trail but found the task too strenuous. There was nothing to do but settle down on a nearby stump and let memory foot the old path.

Strange, but she had only begun to reminisce her way down the trail when she seemed to hear voices of song coming from the heart of The Long Path. What you don't hear when silence falls. It came, of course, from the outdoor chapel which the early settlers had cleared and prepared for an occasional Sunday afternoon service. Ingrid remembered the platform her father had built for the visiting preacher, the man with the guitar, and other participants in the service. Boards had been nailed between the trees as pews for the older folk. What high moments had been spent in this woodland sanctuary! What newness of life had been experienced here!

"If you want to hear God speak," Pastor Berg would say, "come to God's outdoor temple under the open sky, where the roof is high enough to mount up with wings as an eagle."

Though all material evidence of the chapel in the woods was now lost amid the windfalls of time, Ingrid seemed to catch the far-off sound of voices coming from its grounds. There was the song which used to set the whole timberland singing, announcing the glorious day of the Lord's return for His own. How they sang!

> *O härliga dag, som randas för mig!*
> *O härliga mål på pilgrimens stig!*
> *Min längtan och blick allt mer till dig drag,*
> *Du härliga Jesu Kristi dag!*

Ingrid recalled the scene. How suddenly the spirit of these early settlers was transported from the drudgery and hardship of their lot into the ecstasies of that day of days. It was real! They sang believingly. There was the quality of expectancy in their voices. The pent-up rapture deep in their souls found its articulation in this song, and beside this country road heaven dipped down to earth.

Ingrid continued her meditations, reviewing page after page of remembrance with deep pleasure.

Strange what the ear will hear when you become silent and your mind is free.

Suddenly she became aware that the day was beginning to lean toward late afternoon and she must soon be on her way back. How rich had been these hours.

But the old road—it was now a desolate, narrowing strip of sand winding in stillness along the foot of the aged forest. Having retired from life, no new voices come to disturb its peace. Erased are the footprints of children and the boot marks of the early settler. The deep ruts of wagon wheels are seldom seen, and the trails which once played hide-and-seek along the way are blocked by evergreens of a new generation. Across the Big Slough, at the end of the journey, the Corduroy Road lies limp and speechless, sunk in the deep grasses of the marsh.

Ingrid was aware that another highway now spans the countryside in a strait-laced, disciplined manner. It is a wide open roadway where cars meet and pass with amazing efficiency, high tension, and, at times, the shrill shriek of brakes. There is no time for adventures in deep thought. Gone is the solitude and peace of the country lane where the soul found paths to high vistas of insight. *Ja, ack,* the old road—here was a library of many volumes, proclaiming "what the centuries have to say against the hours."

The long fingers of sunset beckoned through the forest aisles, and Ingrid rose from her log, whispered farewell to the old road, and started for town.

# 6. THE CEMETERY

Ingrid had stood in wonder beside the never silent, never uncommunicative lake, a landmark which never changed. She had walked the main street of the little town and searched with bittersweet longing for the markings of the past and present. Today she would turn her face southward and follow the road which led to the quiet hill where the assembly of departed ones lay at rest. If the town and its former life and activities had slackened their pace, the cemetery a mile or so up from town was fulfilling its purpose.

Ingrid remembered when there had been no public burial ground. She recalled dimly the little grave dug in the young sapling forest at the edge of the homestead clearing and the graves that later were scattered among the young evergreens near the end of the road to town. Now the dead lay side by side in the measured lots of a large, ever-expanding field. Often enough there flowed across the countryside the slow tolling of a bell announcing that another earth-worn member of the little settlement had joined the fellowship of the dead.

Far below the sloping landscape the broad blue waters of the Great Lake called to the sleeping meadow in eternal tones. One could feel a mystical communication between the two. Deep calling unto deep. Each had its own message, whether in sound or silence.

Ingrid entered the cemetery as one treading the aisle of a sanctuary after the organ prelude has begun. Here were a few tombstones rising in dignity, neatly cut and polished, casting a spell over the entire field. But many of the dead rested under wooden crosses, or markers, hewn by the loving hands of someone left behind.

The November afternoon held all the funereal shades of late autumn. A ray of sunlight pushed aside the heavy portieres of the sky for a comforting moment, then drew back, and the sigh of a wind was heard again.

Suddenly she caught the sound of a voice—words which held the sweep of the forever in them.

"I am the resurrection, and the life: he that believeth in me, though he were dead, yet shall he live."

The words seemed to come from another world. They floated down the bare November countrystead until they were caught up by the great waters below. Whispering back came the sigh of a great Amen.

"I am the resurrection, and the life"—she had heard these immortal words as far back as she could remember while standing in a circled group beside the final scene in the drama of earthly existence. *"Jag är uppståndelsen och livet."* She could hear again the slow Swedish cadences in the preacher's voice.

Treading carefully over the seams of brown earth, she looked for familiar names—names of loved ones she had known in childhood; names of men and women who had planted seeds of holy influence in the lives of those about them, words and deeds that had lived and grown and brought forth harvest. Poignant tokens of remembrance rose within her as she stood beside the silent sepulchers. She would knock on doors and call out: "Lazarus, come forth!"

It was fitting she should pause first at the graves of her parents, near enough to the main road for passers-by to read the inscription on the monument: "Prepare to meet thy God." Amos 4:12. These were the words she herself had chosen when selecting a tombstone after her father's death. This was neither poetry nor classic utterance. The words from Amos, the prophet, were simple and direct, but they contained the urgent message of her father's life.

"Prepare to meet thy God." In life he had proclaimed the ordinances in the manifold ways in which he witnessed and served his community. To anyone passing the graveyard along the highway he still spoke—"Prepare to meet thy God." Perchance, thought Ingrid, it might slacken the pace of some restless traveler and plant in his mind a seed of serious thought.

51

Ingrid paused to whisper a prayer of thanksgiving beside her parents' grave, recalling again the courage and resourcefulness of her mother, her self-sacrifice, her hopes and dreams. Now she was resting.

Neighbors in life . . . neighbors in death. And a little path between. Ingrid stepped back from the graves of her parents to the next lots. And who should be resting there but their old neighbors, the Isaksons. As in their earthly setting along the shores the Isakson homestead lay to the west of the Hansons, so also in this land of death. The beloved path that had once led to the glories of an only neighbor was now transferred and shortened to a step or two. On that great resurrection morning they will arise together and accompany one another on that heavenly flight which they had so often proclaimed in song. Neighbors in life . . . neighbors in death. And neighbors on the road to glory.

Ingrid crossed several burial spaces and paused beside a marker on which was inscribed the name of Charley Hogberg. To old and young he had carried the name Charley. A friendly person was Charley and especially loved by children. Ingrid recalled when the telephone system came into the settlement. It was Charley who climbed the tall poles and strung the wires across the land. He and the towering posts became as one. Children looked with fear and wonder at the man perched high against the sky in the process of fixing "linjen," as he called it. That was a great day when the shining wires streaked off to far places, laughing and singing in the sunshine, whimpering in the winds of winter.

But in Ingrid's chest of memories was another framed recollection of Charley. The many years had not faded the scene of that long-ago, stormy afternoon in November. She recalled the fury of the west wind and the heaving billows of the lake as they roared toward shore. Then from somewhere up along the beach, in the very heart of the storm, came a voice—a song. At times it faded, only to rise again and then be lost. It was a Swedish song floating on the winds, rising in crescendoes, softening, dying, then returning again. Ingrid had hurried down to the shore that Sunday afternoon to try to discover the mystery of it all, and who should be coming around the bend of the beach but Charley. Drawing closer, his voice rose in strength. There was a quality of finality in the tones which caused her to hear more than the melody, even more than the words. It came from a depth of resolve. It spoke of an anchorage, a soul in the haven of rest.

> *Hur stormarna gny*
> *Under mörknande sky*
> *Hos Jesus jag är i förvar.*

It was a transcendent moment—storm-dark skies ... November ... a song.

And standing beside the grave of old Charley, Ingrid bowed her head in thanks for the memory.

There were many other graves she paused beside, graves of significance to her. She lingered at the sunken bed where the first village organist lay at rest. How he had poured wonder into her young soul as he drew eternity from the bosom of the old reed organ in the Lutheran church as well as in the Mission Friends' place of worship. One could not easily recognize the genius of the man who spent six days behind the meat counter of the village store. But on Sunday morning, when he set off for church dressed in his best, there was a certain grace and stateliness in his walk that would well classify him as an artist. His simple, yet artful, performances on the reed organ introduced to the toilers of the soil another kind of music than that of bird song, wave song, or the chime of a cow bell. Ingrid remembered the spell that fell upon the listener, the comfort that came to the broken hearted, the inspiration that touched the deep reaches of the heart when this man's soul touched the keys of the old organ. Some day he will play again.

Then there was Johanna's grave. Johanna, the meadowlark who in all weather served her fellow men with her songs of trust and courage. Ingrid could still hear the song that poured through the autumn woods as Johanna made her way down to the families on the shores on a certain September day back in the years.

> *Jag blott väntar till dess skördens*
> *Sista kärva bärgats in.*
> *Nu är sommartiden ändad*
> *Och ren blåser höstens vind.*

Johanna did not leave this earth with her faith unsung.

As Ingrid walked toward the center of the burial ground, she came to the grave of Annie, Isakson's Annie. How often in childhood they had walked the long road together to attend school. In rain or sun, storms and deep snows, their strength of body and spirit had been put to test. Annie had learned early in life to assume responsibilities, being the oldest in a family of nine children. "I must see after the children," was her response when someone challenged her to come out and play hide-and-seek in the bushes.

The little frame house in town where Annie spent her married life and, sometime later, her widowhood still stands on a side street looking out upon the sweeping marsh. From her kitchen window Annie had daily viewed the Great Lake beyond the bog. Seated here on a Sunday afternoon, after a week of hard work, Annie's thoughts gave way to sober concerns as she looked into wide spaces. She saw more than the lake and the waving grasses of the slough. On a winter afternoon she saw more than the large pond of ice below, where the town's youth were skating in gay circles. She saw the fields of China and Alaska, of Russia and its hungry people living in sickness and darkness. She saw their poverty and their heathendom. She heard their sigh. And few ears ever caught the Macedonian cry as did Annie's. To the little jar on her frugal pantry shelf was added coin after coin which could well have served her own needs. At the time of her death Ingrid was told that Annie, in spite of her own poverty, had been one of the greatest givers to missions in the entire community. "We can never help heal the need that we do not feel ourselves," she once said as she dropped another piece of silver in her pantry jar. "And some seed fell on good ground and brought forth fruit."

Ingrid bowed her head for a moment, then walked slowly away from Annie's grave.

A few steps away she came to the tomb of the one called Grandpa Lind. No one recalled this saint of

God without a mellowing of the heart. He had been a quiet, humble man more interested in the welfare of others than of himself. In his late years he lived alone in a narrow-shouldered house at the upper end of town. No one ever came in contact with Grandpa Lind without feeling the presence of something more than the man himself. No one met him without nodding in reverence or conversed with him without adding a sterling truth to his thought life. Ingrid had often heard folk say of Grandpa Lind: "There is a Christian."

In his lean-to kitchen, where he spent the larger part of the day keeping the woodfires crackling in his cookstove, his thoughts were often centered on invisible matters pertaining to the great hereafter. Often he returned to the table by the window where he and his open Bible found companionship. Ingrid knew the picture was not an uncommon one in the late years of a saintly life—a fireside, a table with the open pages of a Bible, a lamp, a lone man—or woman—in meditation. And silence.

But should a visitor by chance have knocked on Grandpa Lind's door, he would have been admitted to an atmosphere of warmth and joyous welcome. In the time of old age such visits became rare. Ingrid knew of the dwindling process as, one by one, old friends are severed from the ties of earth. And the footsteps on the threshold, the knock on the door, become fewer and fewer.

Ingrid whispered a prayer of thanksgiving for the life of this man of God and concluded her visit with the friends on the silent hill south of town.

Once out on the main highway she paused to look back. Truly she had knocked on the door of more than one Lazarus that afternoon, and for a golden moment each one had shed his grave clothes and come forth alive.

In the west a trace of sunset appeared on the November sky. Its glow fell across the brown hillside like a sweet benediction on the day. "I am the resurrection, and the life: he that believeth in me, though he were dead, yet shall he live."

# 7. THE BIG SCHOOL

A breath of oncoming winter was in the air that November morning. Out of the mist which hung heavily over the Great Lake a flock of sea gulls appeared, heading south, taking the sky lane over the Big School and disappearing beyond the burial hill south of town.

*Ja,* think, the Big School. This was the day Ingrid was planning to commune with the old landmark which held so many fadeless scenes from early years. She must enter its portals once more and re-experience some of those rare moments which glow on the hearthstone of memory.

She chose the lane which passed the little home where her friend Annie had lived before she took her flight to higher mansions. Annie—Isakson's Annie, and once a childhood neighbor of Ingrid. As she paused in front of the house, she found herself suddenly waving her hand, for in that fleeting moment Annie seemed to be standing by the bay window, greeting Ingrid with a heaven-born smile. Then she was gone. Strange the flow of sensations that come when you walk the paths of the yesteryears. Here are pages of remembrance which hold deep pleasures as well as heartaches. They come, not so much because of specific recallings, but because something sweetly alive has gathered around the memory, creating moods and atmospheres which transfigure the solemn years that come later. It is the glory of old age to remember. It is one of the rich rewards which shine in the evening of life. How well she knew.

Ingrid turned her gaze eastward to the corner where another dwelling had once stood. It was the home that housed the woman who so bruskly refused to let her come near her door when, as a young girl, she was selling thimbles to buy a winter coat. How long she had remembered that cold, wintry noon hour. But age has a way of mellowing the bitter disappointments of the past so that even these add color to life in later years.

As she neared her destination, the sky suddenly began to brighten, and the Big School shone with magnificence in the morning sun. It was a smile of welcome, to be sure.

*Ja, ack,* the Big School. It had been conceived in conflict. Its beams and rafters had risen to the murmur of opposition and complaint.

"Why was not the little country school house good enough for a community so small and so poor?"

"Why go to such extremes—*övermåttan*—so out of keeping with their day?"

"Isn't it better to train the children how to use their hands instead of sitting all day on a school bench with a pile of books?"

*Ja,* so they had gone on. Ingrid could still hear their "reasonable" arguments.

But in the end the few with longer vision and stronger faith won the battle. And while the building ascended in all its glory, from the sturdy foundation to the lofty bell tower, the conflict smouldered. It is ever thus as life expands, thought Ingrid. Always there are the few whose less distorted view enables them to see the distant fulfillments. And led by their vision, they go forth to achieve.

She paused at the gate of the surrounding playground to admire once more the impressive structure in which so large a part of her own life had been spent. The stately edifice, as it rose in height, width, length, and splendor, stood like a misplaced stranger amid the small, apologetic dwellings of the town, but in the space of years it was to prove its worth, not only to the immediate community but to the localities beyond the boundaries of its own township.

Ingrid pushed back the years to the graduation evening of 1907 when a class of boys and girls, including herself, had completed eight years of schooling and were to stand on the impressive platform of the school auditorium and receive their diplomas. It was an honorable occasion—the night that marked the consummation of eight years of study. Ingrid felt certain that no university graduate in the big city could feel the glory of attainment as much as did the eighth-grade country youth and their parents that night. To be sure, there were boys and girls whose schooling concluded before the eight years were up.

The soil, fields, herds, and winter wood cutting demanded their early strength and time. The graduating class was looked upon with both pride and sadness, high expectations as well as some regrets that so many years had been spent in the schoolroom.

But on this particular evening in the budding month of May the Big School drew the people to its bosom like a magnet, and the squeak and rattle of wagon wheels could be heard from every direction as they entered town from the various roadways. Now it was good to have the Big School as it towered over the darkening seaport where tonight there was not a single lamp-lit window to indicate that anyone was absent from the great event at the upper end of town.

*Ja, ack,* this night was different. To crown the occasion there was a brass band which sat grouped on both sides of the main entrance to the building. Ingrid recalled how the instruments glittered in the sunset glow. The sound of horns and trumpets flowed like a newly-awakened stream across the land. Here was wonder. Many were the feet that walked the boarded sidewalk to the rhythm of the big drum and entered the open doorway of the school walking on air. A Sousa march rang through the quiet twilight, followed by "Columbia, Gem of the Ocean" and simple folk songs with definite stroke and color. How the feet of old and young marched to its beat. Last of all came the full, majestic tones of "America," and with that the program in the auditorium of the Big School was about to commence. A great night had descended upon the little town by the seaside.

It was none other than Ingrid's own father, a leading member of the school board, who presided at the presentation of diplomas. Despite his limited English vocabulary, he paid his respects to the graduates in an eloquent, yet serious, manner, not failing to stress the fact of life's brevity, its importance, and the need of a higher wisdom to chart one's course.

*Ja,* that was then. It all came back to Ingrid as she paused in the quiet of the morning before the Big School. Then she left her earliest reveries outside, opened the door, and climbed some steps; there across the center hall was the southwest corner room where for several years she had tried to teach innocent first-graders the a-b-c's of the human adventure. She seemed to hear the echoes of children's voices, and for a long moment the days of her youth came back again. Once more the schoolday scene unrolled. It was nine o'clock in the morning, and she stood before a sea of some thirty faces, each in his own seat in one of the four long rows of desks in the room. As she observed her pupils with hands folded on their desks and every eye looking trustfully into hers, as only the innocent young can do, she felt again the challenge that a teacher experiences as she faces the new school day. She heard herself announce: "Shall we begin this day by singing about the friendly sun?" As Ingrid stood in the room, reviewing the past, she noticed how the sun's beams stole into the room just as it had in the decades long past. She saw each child straighten up in his seat, prepared to sing:

*Good morning, merry sunshine.*
*How did you wake so soon?*

63

*You waken all the birds and beasts*
*And shine away the moon.*

*I saw you go to sleep last night*
*Before I ceased my playing.*
*How did you get way over there,*
*And where have you been staying?*

*I never go to sleep, my child,*
*I just stay round to see*
*The little children of the East*
*Who rise and watch for me.*

*I waken all the birds and beasts*
*And flowers on my way,*
*And last of all the little child*
*Who stayed up late to play.*

How heartily they had sung this song, with voices of many qualities and imperfections. But there was an inner beauty released. It was reflected in their faces.

Ingrid's eyes swept around the room to the blackboard along the east wall on which many young imaginations had found expression. She thought she could still see the chalk drawing which one of her boys had made back in 1912 when the famous ship, the *Titanic*, had met its sad destiny on that fatal April day. How this event had impressed the children of the Big School. It stirred young imaginations, and Ingrid's talented Dan helped to deepen the impression by illustrating the story with a piece of chalk on the board. Who could ever forget the ship that traveled across the billows of the blackboard toward its terrible fate? *Ja, ack*—the *Titanic*.

Ingrid's mind turned back from the blackboard scene to the procedure of the school day. There was always the roll call which followed the morning song:

Aldor Isakson? Ernest Morrison? Dale Burnside? Alice? Ellen? Clara? Helen, Mary, and Waldon were absent.

*Ja*, that was then. Where are they today? Youth, whose white sails had set off so gallantly across the ocean of life, was now approaching harvest years. Scattered throughout the northwest, they are dreaming of a great returning to the shores of childhood where they will set up their homes again within view and sound of the great waters. Here in retirement they hope to recapture the beauty and peace of early years, to feel again the security of a land once blessed by the faith of its founders. And, at last, to embark upon that final journey of mystery to the resting place on the green hill south of town. Already many family members and childhood friends were here at rest.

At rest. *Ja*, think. There was Hilma Johnson, who sat in the second seat of the third row in Ingrid's classroom. Who could ever forget Hilma and her song? In her teen years she dedicated both her life and her voice to the service which counts for time and eternity. Who could not still feel the high reach of her soul as she expressed in her theme song her new-found love—

*On a hill far away stood an old rugged cross,*
*The emblem of suff'ring and shame;*
*And I love that old cross where the dearest and*
*    best*
*For a world of lost sinners was slain.*

A wider field of service began later when Hilma became the wife of a Missionary Alliance preacher and together they traveled the way of consecration and sacrifice, proclaiming the message of that cross. Many souls found their way to Calvary through their ministry. Though Hilma's earthly journey ended in the noon of life, the echoes of her song could still be heard. Ingrid paused in the schoolroom to breathe a prayer of thanksgiving for the little girl who had once sat in the second seat of the third row.

*Ja,* out of this house of learning had sprung green blades of promise. Ingrid recalled the year when the school first offered grammar-school graduates an opportunity to enter higher levels of learning and a high school curriculum was added. There were empty rooms on the second floor which had been foresightedly planned for the purpose of giving ambitious students a chance to go on.

It was a humble number that composed the first high school graduating class after four years of study. Only two—Ingrid's brother Emil and his friend George. But it was a great event for their parents the evening when the two boys received their rolls of parchment. Here was another milepost in the history of the little seaport. Ingrid recalled her mother's pride as they rode home from school that night. Too full for words, she kept her silence. But there was a certain light in her face, the kind that spreads across the human countenance when a high dream has seen fulfillment, a prayer has found its answer. Not until they turned the last corner of the road near home did she give utterance to her feeling: "*Ja,* can you think!" That was all she said. Ingrid could still hear the deep, satisfying sigh and the four Swedish words—*"Ja, kan du tänka!"*

But the first high school graduates had their dreams. As they stood on the platform, holding their well-earned diplomas that eventful evening, they knew that theirs was not a finished task. Their pursuit of knowledge must go on. In the fall of the same year they left the shelter of home and family and set off for the big city. With no one to lean on for assistance, there followed long years of sacrifice and struggle. Laboring with hand and mind, they went from state normal school to college, teaching at intervals to pay their way to a large eastern university. Having finally attained the highest degree in their chosen field, they were ready for the work which awaited them.

As Ingrid stood reminiscing that morning in the high school room on the second floor, a surge of pride swept over her that two home-town boys were now listed among the nation's contributors to the field of education. Two country boys setting out in life, each with an empty purse, a patched wardrobe, a far-off goal, and a will to work—here was greatness.

*Ja, ack,* she sighed, out of this school of humble beginnings had come men and women of strength. There were many who could not dream of professional attainments, for they were needed at home to help shape small clearings into fields that must be plowed and sown and harvested. Always there are the ones who must remain at home to keep a light in the window facing the road, the fires burning on the hearth, and a door unlatched for the returning one. Here, too, is greatness—noble greatness.

But through the years a growing number followed

in the steps of the first two high school graduates. Out of the little town beside the Big Sea waters have come teachers, bankers, artists, musicians, business men, farmers, tradesmen. With imaginations nourished from early childhood by sunsets and starlight, pine song and forest solitudes, snowdrifts and northwest winds—*ja, ack,* there had been a chance to think, to listen, to resolve, to set one's face against the tempest and, nerved by its buffetings, to grow!

Above all there had been the message of the church. There were times when some noted servant of the Lord felt prompted to visit the little village by the seaside. Then it was that the auditorium of the Big School was converted into a sanctuary and crowds too large to be housed in the little red church packed the larger temple with eagerness and, often times, with curiosity. A new face, a new voice—*ack,* who would not come to see and listen?

Lofty moments of heavenly visitation had often been experienced in this sanctuary of learning. Moved by the spirit of an unseen current, the speaker had called to remembrance the life which lay beyond earth's little day. And for the moment tillers of the soil forgot their growing fields and herds and fell to sober meditation on the matter of life's brevity. *Ja, ack,* who could deny the fact of death? But when the speaker introduced a great hope—the inheritance of heavenly places in Christ Jesus—*ja,* that was something else. Although they knew that God's truth has no outworn paths, some let the seed fall along the wayside to be gathered by the fowls of the air. Yet some there were whose heart cries found an answer, whose hungry souls found nourishment and rest.

*Ja,* the Big School had spread its sheltering wings

over gatherings of many purposes and activities. At last Ingrid slowly descended the stairway to the front entrance of the building and closed the door behind her.

The November day which had begun in gloom was now in full burst of noontide sunlight. As she reached the main walk, she paused to look back. From some deep sanctum within her soul she heard a whispered prayer:

"The Lord make His face to shine upon thee, Big School."

# 8. THE LITTLE RED CHURCH

The church which at one time reverently graced the sunny corner lot along the west lane of town was no more to be seen. Leaving the Big School, Ingrid set her face in the direction of the empty lot where this landmark of another day had once stood. She was surprised to discover that the square of holy ground on which it had been built was now a garden of blooming plants. It seemed fitting that on this sacred spot a note of worship should continue to rise as blossoms of many varieties unfolded their petals to the mid-day sun. Even in November several plants were still in brave blooming.

70

The little red church. To Ingrid there had never been a church like it, the first church to open its doors to her childhood. But here was a world she could never enter again. Here were recollections, blurred somewhat by time, but recollections steeped in feelings. Here man had felt God's hand on the latch as he opened the door to enter. Within its walls God's voice had spoken words of comfort as well as words of warning. Tears of sorrow had fallen freely in this temple of God. But tears of joy had also been shed as barriers between God and man had melted away. Sometimes a heaven-born song had been the key which opened the stubborn lock to a hardened heart. Here had come forgiveness and a new sense of direction, and men and women had come away ready to assume their burdens with white sails lifted.

It was here where folks had gathered around a loved one for the last time. It was in this sanctuary that Ingrid had looked once more upon her father's face before the final journey to the green hill south of town.

Like all the churches of early American history its outward charm lay in its primitive simplicity. The four walls were painted red on the outside, giving the church its name—the little red church. There was no denominational name attached to it, although it had been built by some members belonging to the Presbyterian communion. After they left the settlement when the logging industry came to an end, the red church stood empty, waiting for anyone who might come to worship within its fold.

It had but one door. This opened directly into the one and only room—the sanctuary. Here were no halls, vestibules, or foyers. One walked from the outer steps right into the church, blew out one's lantern if it was evening and set it along the back wall with all the other lanterns—Isakson's, Hogberg's, Johnson's, Hammerstrom's, and several more—which had lighted the way to the evening service.

As Ingrid stood on the familiar corner, she saw it all again—the large box stove whose crackling birch fires greeted one on a cold winter night; the home-made pulpit on the low platform, the preacher's kitchen chair behind it; three kerosene chain-lamps hung in the ceiling over the one aisle. On each of the two long walls three windows looked out upon the countryside. On the north one saw the sprawling slough and beyond that the vast stage of water on which sea vessels of many descriptions played their various parts. The view added a background of enrichment to many a hymn that was sung.

But the little red church had one distinctive attraction which Ingrid would always remember. Fitted skillfully into the upper arch of each window were three small, triangular panels of glass, frosted in rich blues, reds, and yellows. While the church was being constructed, someone with creative instinct had felt the need for a touch of sabbatical beauty. Though unlearned in the ways of art, he designed this simple combination of colored glass, hoping to brighten the sober atmosphere of the plain house of worship.

Three panels of colored glass pointing skyward—who could know what fascination they might hold out to a young child's mind and heart? How many tired mothers had lifted their eyes to the tapering window top as they sang of "The Home Over There." As the sun shone through the frosted panes, it spread a diversity of color tones across the room, adding an element of otherness to the atmosphere of worship.

Ingrid recalled the hymns they so often chose to sing. There were many diverse natures behind the worshippers but when certain favorite numbers were announced, they became as one. In the message of the words they sang out their burdens. The gentle, drawn-out melody eased the weight on each singer's heart. But when the song surged like a wave, swelling louder and louder until it seemed to push through the very walls out into the night, every voice, young and old, flowed into the common tide. In those high moments there was no distance between heaven and earth.

Ingrid recalled the song about the well of water which was always open and free for the taking—*"En källa öppen och fri."* She had rarely understood the deeper meaning of the hymns which were sung, but she was intrigued by the pictures they contained. Here was fodder for young imaginations. A well of water. Only a few of the early settlers were fortunate enough to discover this much-sought-for blessing on their acres of land. Once found, they built their log cabins close to it. But many a housewife had to lug her buckets of water from a distant pond or brook, oftentimes at the foot of a deep ravine. With snow to melt in the winter and a barrel of rain water to draw on in summer, they always managed, but with many a sigh. Ingrid's mother had to set off daily for the Great Lake with her pails for water which was anything but clear until the floating debris settled to the bottom of the pail. *Ja, ack.* But sing they did, both heartily and longingly:

*Oss en källa har Gud beredt,*
*En källa öppen och fri.*

There were many songs whose imagery and melody seemed to have been fashioned for the simple tiller of the soil. If the song happened to be "A little while and we'll meet on the heavenly strand," who would not call to mind the golden thread of light seen on the opposite shore of the lake in the dark of night? To Ingrid the "valley of death" could be none other than the deep ravine a mile east of her home. When the script mentioned "lifting mine eyes to the hills," there appeared the towering hill, almost touching the sky, where old man Talbot lived. The beautiful Canaan "beyond the stormy Jordan" was the distant shore across the heaving billows, seen on a clear October day. And the calm of the Galilean Sea was the Great Lake on a quiet Sunday afternoon. *Ja, ack.* The little church on the west lane of town had held in its bosom many songs and sermons, many scenes and facets of feeling. These had woven their patterns on the looms of time.

Many memories came trailing back as Ingrid stood beside the vacant lot that November afternoon. She thought of the many Sunday afternoons when she and the neighbor children—Annie and Isak—had walked the long miles to attend Sunday school in the red church. Summer or winter, springtime or harvest, it had been the happiest walk in the years. Rolled up in their hands was the Swedish quarterly which contained the lesson and memory verse for each Sunday.

"Well, did you learn your *tänkespråk* for today?" Ingrid would ask Annie. And Annie would recite 1 Cor. 13:13, the verse about the greatest virtue in life, which is love:

*"Men nu förbliva tro, hopp, kärlek, dessa tre, men störst ibland dem är kärlek."*

They did not always grasp the full content of the memorized Scripture verse, but they knew something about this one, about love—*kärlek*—for the teacher who met them at the door of the red church every Sunday afternoon was a clear illustration of the word "love." It was bachelor Ernst Johnson, the man who stood behind the counter in the village store six days out of the week. No child missed his attention. He used every opportunity to show his love and interest for the boy or girl who came across his path. Ingrid had often wondered why so many grown-ups failed to take time to express their interest and affection in word and action. Good they could be, helpful and honest, but not well-versed in the warm, delicate language of love. But when Ernst Johnson laid his hand on your shoulder and smiled into your eyes, God's love poured through too. Somewhere in his life he had learned the heart-need of the young.

Many were the kindnesses he showed the child who stepped inside the store on his way home from school. Many were the treats he handed over the counter to the boy or girl who looked hungrily at the candy sticks or Mary Ann cookies in the showcases. Often he stopped to tie some child's shoe or to pin the coat collar whose button had come loose. Always there were the kind words of encouragement and strength that sent the child on his long homeward journey knowing he had a friend. *Ja,* here was something to remember, something destined to remain alive, to help him rise to his best. What a great part

Ernst Johnson had played in the history of the little red church.

Ingrid liked to think of the prayer meetings which were sometimes held in the church in town. During the howling winds of winter, when snow fell heavily over the countryside, it had served as a more central meeting-place than the log house at some far edge of the settlement. She remembered her father's urgency for fellowship in prayer and his determination to keep the prayer fires burning. Often after a heavy day's toil, cutting trees and sawing logs, he would walk the many miles to be present at a prayer service. She recalled one such meeting which took place on an evening of early December. In the late afternoon of that day a blizzard had come sweeping across the lake and by evening had whipped up into high fury. The cold winds had moaned and lashed around the corners, but her father was not daunted by winds or blizzards. Ingrid's mother looked disturbed as her husband stepped into his high boots and began buttoning up his ancient, long-haired fur coat. As he was about to leave, she faced him at the door.

"Surely you don't intend to go out on a night like this?"

"*Ja,* say that. That is the question everyone is shudderingly asking right now," he answered. "Out on a night like this? God's work must go on. It is at a time like this when miracles can happen. Someone must face the storms even on a night like this." Then he was off.

It was years later that Ingrid heard the details of that evening. That night when her father reached the church, chilled and breathless, he found everything dark and cold. "It could be early," he reasoned to himself. He had no way of knowing the time. Perhaps he had walked faster than usual. Someone else would surely be coming, for they certainly knew he would be there. He set to work lighting the kerosene lamps in the ceiling and then gathered in birch logs and kindling from the woodpile behind the church.

Down the main street of town two men could be seen thrusting their way against the bitter winds and snows—Hogberg and Lind, neighbors from the upper end of the village.

"*Ack*, what a night," groaned Hogberg. "It will be a miracle if anyone else comes out tonight!"

"*Ja*, talk never about that. You may be sure Hanson will be there if he has to walk on all fours. And I don't envy the one who has to walk the Corduroy Road on a night like this." Lind brushed the snow from his face and looked in the direction of the corner lot along the west lane.

"Look," he exclaimed. "There's a light in the church and smoke curling from the chimney. *Ja*, just as I said, Hanson is already there, you can be sure."

It was good to come in from the cold and draw up to the warmth and light of the little church. Time passed, and when no more footsteps could be heard on the outer steps, it was time to prepare for worship. Then, while the winds howled and whistled around the corners, three men knelt in prayer.

Who could know what miracles took place in the hearts of the three men kneeling beside the big box stove that night as they gave utterance to the deep things within? And who could foresee the far-reaching consequences of these petitions on other lives, perhaps younger lives, up in the years ahead? All be-

77

cause three men had pushed through the storm and blizzard on a night like this—to pray.

Had God been in their midst? *Ack, ja.* This they knew with marvelous clarity. "Where two or three are gathered together in my name, there am I in the midst of them"—Christ must have known that in the centuries to come three men, on a stormy winter night, would be gathered in a remote country church to pray.

*Ja, ack.* The red church had served its day. It had held the echoes of many a prayer, many a song, many a sigh of both longing and gladness. These had written their story on the hearts and minds of the young. And simple men of robust faith had left their prayer-prints on the sands of tomorrow.

# *9.* THE COUNTRY SCHOOL

The ground where it stood is now a barren patch of weeds that tremble in the wind. But the seagulls' cries have never ceased, and something in their call makes time swing back.

As Ingrid stood on the enchanted ground, the scene set deep in the years came to life again—the wind-swept field along the water's edge, waves splashing their accompaniments to the chant of sea birds, a little white schoolhouse throbbing against the blue of sky and sea and waiting for her, the teacher.

It was afternoon when she revisited the sacred spot where the school had once graced the lonely landscape many miles to the west of her homestead settlement. How much the years had erased from the earliest setting of this lakeside port. Even the schoolhouse had finished its story. It had sung its youthful songs, and on its playground could no more be seen the footprints of children's feet. The dwellings which had once stood nearby had also surrendered to desolation. Gone was the mill, the hotel, the saloon. Here and there a roof, from whose chimney warm curls of smoke had risen skyward, lay collapsed between unsteady walls. A little town had died. Its day was over.

There had been a time when life flowed at high ebb along this bend of the shore. Men swung their axes, and giant trees fell to the ground prostrate. Limbs were slashed, and logs were towed to the mill for slicing into towers of fresh, fragrant lumber, then shipped by heavy freighters to worlds of larger ports. Here was poetry. Here was early history set in strong art. At the long day's end the laborer whistled as he walked the lane to his room for the night—"Down by the Old Mill Stream" or "My Darling Nellie Gray." Contentedly the song floated on the evening breezes. All was well at the little seaport.

Upstairs in the simple hotel a room was reserved for worship. Here in the little chapel folks gathered at various times to chant together, over and again:

> *Hail Mary, full of grace,*
> *The Lord is with thee;*
> *Blessed art thou among women.*

Then came the day when the logging industry had finished its natural course, and there was no longer any reason for men to remain here. The busy era trickled away, and the curtain lowered on the final act. Silence brooded over the little lake port.

A small remnant of folk, however, was loathe to

leave, reluctant to see a whole community wiped away. A few families hoped to find a meager livelihood by farming. Some bachelors clung to their crude huts, trying their luck at fishing, trapping, and berrying. One family moved into the empty hotel, which was near enough to the school to board and room the teacher. It was in this turn of history that Ingrid made her appearance.

How well she remembered this chapter in her life. After much sacrifice and hard work, plowing a determined furrow into the field of education at the nearest normal school, she had acquired a certificate which qualified her to teach the elementary grades of a country school. This done, the little schoolhouse on the lakescaped edge of Wisconsin reached out its hand of welcome to her. Forty dollars a month! How would it feel to hold forty dollars in her hand! Too good to believe. Since the new position would be only nine miles from her home, she would be able to spend weekends with her family and townsfolk, providing someone would hitch up the horse on Friday evening and bring the teacher back by Sunday afternoon. How good life had been to her! Her own school, her own monthly check, trips home and back—and all these blessings close to the very heart of the Great Lake.

She remembered the Sunday afternoon when she and her father sat side by side in the front seat of the old wagon, headed for her first school. Summer had accomplished most of its work and was ready to hand over the remainder of its fruiting to autumn. It was a beautiful September day, the trees changing their uniforms of green to garbs of gold, crimson, and russet. Autumn wonder thrilled out to meet them. Birds sang of flights to come when the warning signs of late autumn would appear. A meadowlark filled the quiet intervals with a call to worship. September was in the air, in the beams of the sun, in the tapestries of the woodlands and along the roadsides embroidered thickly in goldenrods and purple asters. September was also in the hearts of the two who sat in the front seat of the wagon, silently journeying up a spiral staircase of many emotions. It was the kind of afternoon that touched all the creative urges within one's soul. Ingrid wished deeply that she could have expressed all she felt as she rode the new, untried miles to her first school. Neither she nor her father voiced their thoughts as they rode the first few miles of their journey. Not until they reached a change in the landscape did her father speak:

"*Ja*, here is where Milton Smith lives." He pointed to a dejected strip of clearing at one side of the road. Its leanness added a minor note to the glad music of the autumn day. An apologetic building stood on the silent acres. There were no curtains in the window, no plants. Grass grew high as weeds along the path to the door. An old fence leaned with fatigue. Poverty can be a darkness.

"They have a little boy here you will very likely have in your schoolroom," he added. A little boy—an uncertain cloud crossed Ingrid's fair sky. A little boy walking all these miles to school looking for light.

"And here is where bachelor Bill Goff holds forth." This time her father pointed to a clean little berry farm up ahead which lay dreaming in the Sunday afternoon sun. The cozy little cabin half-hidden among the trees sent up friendly spirals of smoke which slowly dissolved in the treetops. Here was pleasant September back again.

Her father knew Bill Goff well. Bill raised berries in the summer and trapped fur-bearing animals in the late fall and winter, selling the pelts in the city across the lake. He was an interesting person in his rural way of thinking and produced many a fascinating bit of philosophy for others to remember and quote in good fellowship over their coffee cups. Ingrid had often heard her father speak of Bill Goff. "There is a man content with his lot, at peace with his world. He should be a Christian."

They continued in silence again, with no sign of life save that of a porcupine crossing the road in leisurely manner. Ingrid had sensed they were nearing their destination. A whiff of lake breeze had crossed the road now and then. Through a slit in the forest she caught a faint glimpse of the lake. One more turn and they were headed toward the Great Lake with all its predominance. She could hear the unfailing rhythm of the waves. Before them lay the sprawling hamlet, and off to one side a little white schoolhouse rose challengingly against the blue of the lake, like a ship ready to set sail. Something leaped inside her. There came a moment mingled with both joy and fear, high hopes and a sense of helplessness. She felt desperately her human limitations and the need of wisdom and strength from another source.

The horse and wagon turned down the only lane, passed the abandoned saloon where old Mike still lived, and stopped at the gray, weatherbeaten hotel building. They were greeted by the kind family who occupied the first floor. Here in the large waiting room, or lobby, loggers had once sat on long winter evenings spinning fireside stories of days gone by and scanning the future through the thick mists of their smoking pipes.

Ingrid was shown to a room upstairs next to the chamber which was still used as a Catholic sanctuary and in which stood an altar, a cross, and a statue of Mary. A few chairs served as pews for the worshippers.

Ingrid's room looked out upon a singing river which flowed through the mouth of the channel and on into the lake. Here was charm, a retreat made for dreaming, meditating, praying. From the west windows at night could be seen the same fine thread of gold which had always given such mystic tugs at her being. From the same windows the late day spread a glorious screen of sunset. Here was much to awaken illumination, imagination, and worship.

The Sunday evening supper, to which her father, too, had been invited, was a pleasing occasion in company with Mr. and Mrs. Kent, their three children, and the Irish grandfather who addressed Ingrid as "tacher," with a drag on the long "a," the name by which she would always be known by him. Before the meal was served her father bowed his head in prayer, asking God's blessing on the food, the home, and community, and, last, upon the school which was about to commence another year. Ingrid detected a tenderness in his voice as he mentioned the school. There was eloquence in the prayer that sprang from his heart in spite of his limited English vocabulary.

The day was being cloaked in twilight when Ingrid said goodbye to her father. How well she remembered his leaving, his words of encouragement. She could still see him headed homeward along the rutted, clay-hardened road, the rattle of wagon wheels the only sound against the tranquility of the Sunday evening. Its echoes imposed a spell upon the silent countryside, so new, so strange.

Once her father had driven beyond hearing, a feeling of loneliness fell over her, a loneliness which comes when one is about to face the unknown. Everything but herself seemed strong—the lake with its blue immensity, trees thick and tall, new faces looking into hers. She decided to walk over to the little building where she was destined to spend the next eight months of her late teen years. She must introduce herself to this new post. The next day would be Labor Day, and on Tuesday, the first Tuesday of September, 1911, she would come face to face with a small group of boys and girls full of silent questions. Her first school.

It was a pleasant walk to the school in the still of the evening. But she could feel already the free play this open path across the meadow would afford the northwest winds of winter. It would require the same strength and determination that was once expended on the old Corduroy Road back home. But this night nature treated the new teacher with kindness and respect.

She paused beside the school building to study the magic circle which surrounded it. Here were maples, oaks, and birches reflecting all the glories of the dying sunset. On the lakeward side the immense stage of waves rendered an evening sonata, the constant and intriguing fugue she had heard from early infancy.

She opened the door somewhat prayerfully and stepped through a hallway which led to the main assembly, where two rows of desks occupied half of the floor space. On the opposite side, near the back, stood a large, wood-burning stove, cylindrical in shape and with a ruffle of nickel lace around its base. The woodbox beside it was already filled with chunks of birch and kindling bark. Out in the hall a well-filled pail of lake water stood on a bench, a common dipper hanging on the wall beside it. The three windows on each side of the classroom were bare and bleak. There was need of curtains to be put up and pots of flowering geraniums set in the sills to brighten the atmosphere. Her schoolroom must have an atmosphere of happiness if the best work was to be achieved. There was need of maps and charts for the bare walls, and she must find some meaningful nature scenes and pictures of great men to render inspiration and vision to young minds. There must be a certain invasion of wonder, of delight, as the children entered the room on a gray morning. This would be their world—and hers.

Ingrid recalled a vivid scene from her own childhood. How often she had dreamed of standing before a class of boys and girls, opening their minds and hearts to new worlds, drawing answers from them, sharing stories of great men and women, awakening wonder. How she had loved to play the game of teacher when no one was around. Many were the times when her mother, returning from the evening chores, found the kitchen floor unswept and the supper dishes unwashed. There would be stern words, but never did Ingrid explain that while her mother was milking cows, she, Ingrid, was teaching a class in history, or geography, in the front room, where a semicircle of chairs had been arranged, each chair bearing the name of a boy or girl. What fun she had experienced standing before this imaginary class. She had changed her tone of voice to that of an adult, giving nods of approval when right answers were given, reprimanding the one who failed to listen, calling each child by name. Lost in the intriguing game of teaching, she had forgotten all about floors and dishes. Not until she heard her mother's steps on the back porch did she send each pupil back to the part of the room where he was wont to stand. She could still recall her mother's swift glance around the kitchen. "I can't understand what you do with your time when I am in the barn. Here stand the dirty dishes and the floor unswept."

Ingrid offered not the faintest clue regarding the hour she had spent in teaching a class how Columbus discovered America or how the Pilgrims celebrated their first Thanksgiving. Her only answer had been "I've been preparing my history lesson for tomorrow." Little did she realize then how many far-off tomorrows were tucked into that answer.

All these memories of teacher-play had returned to Ingrid as she stood in her country school that long-ago afternoon. One more day, and she would face that long-dreamed-of tomorrow. She would stand before her boys and girls, no longer a semicircle of empty chairs but a group of vital, active persons with eager faces looking up into hers. She could hear them ask: "What do you have to give?"

*I am the child.*
*You hold in your hand my destiny.*

*You determine, largely, whether I shall succeed*
    *or fail.*
*Train me, I beg you, that I may be a blessing*
    *in the world.*

Ingrid had known there would be problems, testings, lonely Gethsemanes. She had heard other young teachers speak of the struggles and the loneliness of their first year in a country school. But there would be sources of inspiration and comfort. From the window of that upper room in the rambling hotel would come glimpses of eternal truth. She would learn how the evening star braves through at twilight. There would be the golden promises wrapped up in sunsets, the shining hope in that thread of light across the dark waters at night. And, perchance, from some Mount Nebo's height she might see spread before her vast areas of fulfillment. For she was a teacher.

*The little seed I sowed today*
*Deep in a young child's heart*
*Was strangely blown into my hand*
*From some vast heavenly mart.*
*A tiny seed—and yet I know*
*In some young life it will live and grow,*
*Will live and grow.*

*So help me, God, to climb the heights*
*Where spiritual breezes blow*
*That I may catch some living truth*
*To help a child to grow.*
*Some white-winged deed, or word—I know*
*In some young life it will live and grow,*
*Will live and grow.*

*Ja,* that was then. Suddenly it was night, and Ingrid had become aware that for two hours, or more, she had held a rendezvous with the past. One memory had recalled another, some of which had lain long-forgotten at the bottom of the treasure chest. September, 1911, was a far way back. And now, all at once, the dial of time had turned ruthlessly into the 1960's again. She must leave the scenes of the yesteryears, precious as they are when life is in its yellow leaf. Gone now are the little hamlet on the shore and all its inhabitants. Gone are the schoolhouse and the ones who had sat at her feet learning. Gone are the landmarks of an age. Nothing but echoes flowed back across the barren acres. Here was a stillness both sad and eloquent.

Ingrid had known a high moment of sweet returning to the little country schoolhouse that once stood steepled high against the blue of sea and sky. Her first school.

# *10.* MYSTIC MOMENTS

They came to an opening in the woods which must once have been the very place for which they were looking.

"Shall we stop here for a while?" suggested Ingrid's brother, slowing down the old Dodge. They had set out this afternoon to explore old, forsaken landmarks which in the very bosom of their desolation held the story of early beginnings, the story of days when the infant civilization along the Great Lake first began to breathe, when—miles apart—curls of smoke rose bravely from cabin roofs and the sound of cutting timber rang its prelude through the virgin forest.

They had chugged their way along an old road no longer marked by wagon wheels or footsteps, crushing tall weeds and grasses that had long stood thick and undisturbed.

*Ja, visst,* they must stop here, for this must be it. This must be the place where Sofie Monson's homestead had at one time sent up warm spirals of smoke. But—*ack, ja*—time had tried to erase all semblance of that ancient day.

Ingrid stepped out of the car, her eyes searching for the spot where the friendly log hut had once stood. "Is there anybody there?" she called. Only a strange silence surged back in answer to her call.

Memory is a paradise which rarely shuts its doors. And as Ingrid stood waiting, a door gently opened on a long-ago winter day in her early childhood. She saw Sofie running excitedly down the snowy path to welcome her friends, Mama and Emma and their sled full of little ones, herself included. For hours Sofie had scanned the east window, hoping to see her friends emerge from the thick woods onto her clearing. When at last they appeared, her joy was so great she could not control the high pitch of her emotions. It was a rare day when friends met friends, especially in the winter, living as they did many trackless miles apart.

"You got here, you got here!" she cried, welcoming her friends with open arms. To Emma and Mama, exhausted from the strenuous journey of many difficult miles through deep snow, no greeting could have been sweeter, no destination so rewarding as the warmth and rest awaiting them in Sofie's log hut at one corner of the little clearing.

What a pleasant afternoon they must have spent together, reflected Ingrid, peering through the growth of brush. While she and Emma's little ones were napping in the other room, the women had reviewed together the many dramatic adventures in their days

91

of early homesteading. In the midst of their colorful accounts had come ripples of laughter. How well they understood each other. *Ack*, it had been good to have someone with whom to share the story of home-steading.

Ingrid had forgotten many of the details of that winter day, but one high moment had fixed itself upon her young mind. A feeling once stirred within one is not likely to evaporate. It was the ecstasy of the greeting and the full, deep comfort of having finally arrived.

"You got here, you got here!" She would always feel the overflow of joy which lay in the words that sprang from a lonely woman's heart.

In her maturer years Ingrid had often mused over this childhood incident. It could well be the opening scene awaiting the tired pilgrim at the end of life's journey. Exhausted from drifts of trial and—often-times—trackless miles he emerges from the burdens of earth's wilderness into the sunlit vastness of heaven's clearing. And in that moment he hears the welcome words—"You got here, you got here!"

"Shall we drive west now and see what Johanna's old homestead has to say?" suggested Ingrid.

Panoramas of familiar settings unrolled before them as they drove toward the afternoon sun. Here were scenes which the years had not changed. They reached the hilltop where many a weary traveler had stopped to rest. Far below lay the Great Lake in all its vast majesty. To one side the old Stonequarry Point still stretched its long arm, ever hoping to touch the shore on the distant horizon.

How much can happen to the soul of man, thought Ingrid, when standing on a hilltop! "Climb a hill!"

Pastor Berg had said in one of his sermons while visiting the little community along the lake. "Look at your problems from the heights!" There were several Mount Nebos throughout the land where men and women had paused when the pattern of life had become blurred and they could see their existence only in the light of the common day. A moment on the hilltop had often given breadth to their vision and opened inner channels to higher outlook. They came away wiser for having stood upon the mount with God. As Johanna would say, coming back to the levels of earth, *"Jag kände evigheten där uppe."*

When they reached Johanna's place, they found the old log house on the edge of the ravine desolate and empty. Though still intact, they could see how time had gnawed deeply into its frame.

"Is there anybody there?" Only the echoes of her own voice came through the stillness. To one side of the empty dwelling the feeble apple orchard spoke of life's closing chapter. "Is there anybody there?"

Then from out of another age a door opened, and Ingrid heard a voice. It was Johanna, of course, singing her sunset song.

> *Blott en dag, ett ögonblick i sänder,*
> *Vilken tröst, evad som kommer på!*
> *Allt ju vilar i min Faders händer,*
> *Skulle jag, som barn, väl ängslas då?*

It would be typical of Johanna to choose such a song for this time of day. In the west the sun was making ready to mark the passing of another day with its glorious setting. How fitting was this song of complete trust in her heavenly Father. But Johanna had more than one song. In her repertory of memorized canticles there was a song for every occasion. Come dark days or sunlit ones, come illness, poverty, testings, helplessness—for every feeling within the breast there was just the right song, the key that lifted the burden. Her home had not lost its echoes of song.

But when they turned to leave Johanna's cabin by the edge of the ravine, they were arrested by another voice. It came not out of the yesteryears; it trembled out of the immediate moment. How significant that the visit to Johanna's old home should close on this note.

In the woodland behind the orchard, in the upper branches of a dead oak tree, a late bird caroled an "amen" to the day. In his rhapsody was the same quality of certainty and praise which had always characterized Johanna's song as she sang her way triumphantly through the stress of years.

And in this sunset cadence who could listen long without the urge to kneel in prayer.

* * *

Sunset was still falling over the hillside when they set off for another outpost of the yesteryears. These were the short days, casting the year's deepest melancholy over land and sea.

When they came out of the shelter of the woods, they heard the cry of the oncoming night winds as they rode the Corduroy Road. It was good to enter the silence of Flag River Valley. Four more miles and they would reach the homestead acres where another early settler had once lived.

In Ingrid's youth the trip to Hammerstroms meant going on an exploration to discover how big the world really was. Now, as they traveled along the

94

way, they passed openings in the underbrush which suggested paths which had once led to the ancient lodgings of the bachelors Johnson, Hogberg, Guldstrand, and others. Though a new generation had planted its tracks in the valley and many former things had passed away, something of the early era still clung to each place. It told its own story, it sang its own theme.

When they reached their destination, Ingrid discovered that here, too, another owner was adding his chapter to the history of the old homestead.

"Let's not go farther," she said as they entered the edge of the clearing; "I want to see it all from a distance and through the eyes of childhood."

Even though the character of the place had changed, a door swung open into the early newsettling epoch, and memory unrolled another lofty scene.

It was Christmas in the middle 90's, and there was a *Julotta* service at the Hammerstroms. There had never been such a Christmas since the first one back in the little town of Bethlehem. The still, white night was full of starlight and sky song. Bethlehem lay peacefully spread along the countryside as they rode in stillness through the forest—Ingrid and her family. She would always recall that journey in the early morning.

The Christmas service in Flag River Valley! *Ack, ja.* Some details of it had grown dim, but one towering moment still held its luster. It had taken the riper years to fully appreciate its significance. Here in the little log house along Flag River were folk assembled who had known hardship, privation, illness, and sorrow. But in their world of trial they had discovered paths which led to summits with wide vistas of insight.

It was the closing prayer by Hammerstrom that lifted the Christmas service into realms beyond the boundaries of earth. This simple tiller of the soil had stood beside the very door of death only a few weeks before. There had been no physician to call, no hospital, no medicines to be had. There were, of course, the ever-present standbys found on everyone's cupboard shelf—Ward's Liniment and Dr. Peter's Kuriko. But these were powerless in the face of impending death. In this dark hour there was but one hope to lean on—God.

Not that the early Christian settler looked upon death with fear. The transition from earth to heaven was considered a rapturous experience to the believer. It was often in their thoughts, and it was heard in their conversation. They sang about it with great tenderness and longing. If Hammerstrom had been called to his home up yonder, he would have been ready to go. But all knew how much he was needed here, in his home and community. Just when circumstances seemed to speak of the impossible, the miracle of healing took place, and great was the joy and gratitude of his family and friends. God had answered prayer! The Bethlehem Christ had touched his body with healing and new life. Out of the depths of his heart, on this Christmas morning, came utterances of praise that opened new springs of faith in each listening heart.

There were tears and whispered amens when the prayer drew to a close. For a brief time an arresting silence lay upon the candlelighted room. Someone from another world seemed to be holding this lofty moment in His grasp. And in the spell of its holiness the little assembly of worshipers climbed to summits beyond the borders of earth.

Moments later, as the window shades were lifted, the dawn of a new day could be seen. But greater than the light in the eastern sky was the dawn which had been kindled in the hearts of the worshipers. And when they lifted their voices in the majestic Swedish Yuletide song—"All Hail to Thee, O Blessed Morn"—dawn expanded into a glorious sunrise! Ingrid could still hear them sing as she stood on the edge of the clearing in the dusk of evening:

*Var hälsad, sköna morgonstund,*
*Som av profeters helga mun*
*Är oss bebådad vorden!*
*Du stora dag, du sälla dag,*
*På vilken himlens välbehag*
*Ännu besöker jorden!*

As Ingrid recalled the scene of the *Julotta* service in the 90's, she knew that the little prayer group up in the Flag River Valley had come as close to the Bethlehem morning as they would ever come in this journey through earth. *Ja,* that was then.

## *11.* THE OLD HOMESTEAD

Evening drew the afternoon to a close, and another day was subtracted from Ingrid's visit at the seaport on the shores. Tomorrow she must fulfil the chief purpose of her sojourn here. She must go back to the old homestead by the lake, to the earliest scenes and rarest ecstasies of childhood, back to the place alive with pulsating currents of memories.

She remembered with sadness the crushing sordidness of the old homestead when last seen, several years before. It had lain like a crumbling shell in a tangle of weeds and brush. It was no longer any man's home. Notes of neglect and desolation sounded in the winds that blew against the sagging porch and through the doors that hung half open on bent hinges. A colony of wild animals had left footprints everywhere, and more than one woodchuck had bored his hole under the log foundation. Nature had taken over the place. The walls stood speechless and cold. Bravely the broken window panes reflected the late afternoon sun.

Was this home? Ingrid had asked the question, seeking an answer from the big pine nearby, the woodshed, the grassy marsh—everything on which she fixed her eyes. Was this her old home? Only silence flowed back.

She hesitated to cross the threshold and go inside, choosing rather to find refuge under the comforting arms of the aged mountain ash, a landmark which still stood in its accustomed place between the house and the lake, a guard against the winds. Here she would wait until her inner disappointment and confusion settled. She remembered turning her face to the Great Lake to listen to one of its familiar songs. There was neither joy nor anger in its music that day. Its brooding tones spoke of a strangeness that hovers over time and change, gain and loss, life and death. She had heard it many times in childhood.

Gradually the distance between the past and the present began to shorten. The old homestead lost its remoteness and began to speak—deeply, profoundly.

They were not words she heard that late afternoon. Her listening was for unformed things that come from depths that find no expression—callings which echo through all the tunnels of earthly existence.

Refreshed in perspective, Ingrid finally decided to enter the old home. She pushed back the screeching door and stepped into the kitchen, a wing of the house not made of logs, which her father had added to the original cabin years later. Here stood the old wood range, cold and rusty. There was no fragrance of life within these walls, no cheerful crackle of wood fires, no tempting aroma of Arbuckle's coffee, no clink of cups and saucers and friendly chatter. She stepped into the other room, the room that had been the kitchen in the early years, and tried to revive some of the scenes of the yesteryears. Here they had cooked, eaten, and slept. Along one wall had stood the bench with pails of soft lake water and, close by, the well-fed box of birch wood ready for the approaching morrow. How often on a winter night the snow had piled high against the one and only window. She remembered being lulled to sleep by the south wind piping its lonely melody in the space between the snowdrift and the window panes.

In this room a little sister had been born—and four of her brothers. Anders and Emil had the unmistakable stamp of Sweden on their names. George, who had come later, received a name taken from the American list. And when the last one was born, American patriotism in the log house on the shore had risen to its heights. Called Theodore, he was named after the highly esteemed president of the United States—Theodore Roosevelt.

Ingrid had stepped into the other room—the front room, it was called. Standing there, everything had swept back in a flood of scenes and sounds. This was the company room which served as parlor, sitting room, bedroom, a place to host the traveling preacher who chanced to come, sometimes alone, sometimes in a family group. This was the room which called for your best manners, for smiles and courtesy even though shyness gnawed at your real self, especially if your arrivals were others than the familiar faces of the little settlement.

It was a large, sunny room with two windows facing the one and only neighbor, the only light at night beside your own which spoke of human existence. Another window looked out upon the vast stage of waters where many scenes of great drama were performed with stately charm by all manner of sea-trained actors—portly passenger ships, loaded lumber freighters, frantic little tugboats, scows basking in the distant horizon, rowboats, sailboats. Here was pageantry, splendor, beauty, life!

But when the curtain rose on the ship coming into port—*ja, ack*—here was the loftiest act in the play. How often Ingrid had stood by this lakeward window, waiting for a faint, mysterious speck of life to emerge from a distant smudge of smoke and gradually take on the form of an approaching vessel. Slowly the craft had grown in size until the prow of a stately passenger steamer pointed shoreward—directly at the little face in the log house window. Here was wonder!

How often Ingrid had waited for the closing act. Drawn by the long, outstretched arms of the pier, the ship would set its face majestically toward the peace and safety of the waiting harbor, leaving the uncertain world of waters behind. A ship coming into port is an unforgettable performance. It is a subject for the artist's brush, the poet's song, the preacher's altar call.

Close beside this window with its seaward view was the door that opened to arriving company—to special guests, usually, rather than the folks of the little community. Their knocks were most often heard

101

on the kitchen door. On warm summer evenings the company door might also open to the night-time music of the big pine, nocturnes that spoke of timeless things. Or to the melancholy urgencies of a freighter calling across the dark waters.

Suspended from the ceiling of the room was a large hang-lamp that had once spread its festive glow. Ingrid recalled how the sparkling fringe of crystal prisms had added a note of luxury to the special occasions—city company, a minister's visit, Aunt Augusta's arrival, or even a group of settlers gathered for prayer.

On a bench under the hang-lamp long rows of house plants had added their note of cheer to the room as they smiled in blossoming bells, stars, cups, blood-drops. Born of long association, each plant had grown into a certain kind of personality that changed the atmosphere of winter into the warmth and freshness of spring.

In one corner of the room had stood the friendly Franklin heater over which cold hands had been stretched after a stern winter day. Around this stove conversation began to flow easily, naturally.

And along this wall—*ja,* think. Here had stood the priceless reed organ for which she had traveled the countryside from door to door, selling thimbles, ten dozen thimbles, to make a dream come true. The reed organ! How it had enhanced the happiness of this front room as well as the whole house and all creation around the home. How the birds had joined their twitterings to its simple chordings! How the squirrels and rabbits had stood on hind legs in rapt listening! Even the fowls of the barnyard had drawn

near, tilting their heads in spellbound curiosity!
Here was grandeur, music, worship.

As Ingrid had stood here in the midst of memories, she felt again the atmosphere of childhood Sabbath, the day when one forgot the grime of labor, the strain of hardship. Almost she could hear her father's voice as he sang his favorite song on Sunday mornings. His voice may have quavered and cracked as he gave expression to God's grace coming afresh each morning, but no one could miss the soul-tones that came through.

> *Herrens nåd är var morgon ny.*
> *Varför skulle vi sörja?*
> *Jordens skuggor, hur snart de fly,*
> *Må vår lovsång då börja.*

This front room had held a variety of moods and atmospheres. Ingrid could recall the lofty feel of Easter Sunday, the quiet solemnity of Good Friday, and, not least, the joyous spirit that hovered over Christmas. She looked at the bare corner where the Christmas tree had once stood, the most perfect and shapely balsam in the forest, free for the taking. *Ja,* think—here had been happiness.

From this room had risen many a prayer, carrying heavenward urgencies of soul, heart cries, intercessions, hymns of praise and gratitude. And weary settlers, rising from bended knees, had walked home under the starlit heavens with lifted hearts. Occasionally a song of praise could well have been heard ringing through the forest as they trudged their way homeward. Log cabin prayer meetings were great occasions among the early Christian settlers.

But though the front room had been the lighted wing of the house, the scene of much happiness, it also held memories of sober days when palls of darkness hung heavy over the log cabin on the shores. In this chamber both birth and death had found entrance. It was here that the first funeral service was held when Ingrid's infant sister had slipped off to a fairer shore. Dimly she remembered that spring afternoon and the group of settlers who came to stand beside this solemn occasion—the first death in the settlement on the shores.

It was also in this room that her father had lain silent in his simple wooden coffin on a March day back in the years. Ingrid had been summoned home from her school in the big city. There was no funeral parlor to open its doors for this sad occasion, no undertaker to prepare his body for the last rites. It was Isakson, at the other end of the path, who had come over to make his neighbor ready for his last appearance, when friends would gather around this unfathomable mystery of final departure. If in the past there had been disagreements or hard words between the dead and the living, as was sometimes the case, all had been swept away by the austere presence of death. Only the best came to remembrance. Ingrid had lifted her head and looked into the solemn country faces of the gathered ones. There was T.N., the village leader, standing erect with hat in hand. Silence had been the only speech among the men until T.N. took the lead. There was something epic about his words, about his dramatic recital as he spoke of the loyalty and support the departed one had rendered to all worthwhile undertakings, his willingness to serve, his adherence to Christian principles, his courage to stand alone when others faltered.

There was the village storekeeper, who had found such inspiration in discussing with his brother the Word of God as they leaned over the meat counter in his store.

There was widow Johnson, who more than once had received a silver dollar or a sack of potatoes from the man on the shores. Many others stood around the coffin remembering tender moments, significant acts. And though the odor of death lay heavy upon the room, there was also a spell of wonder.

*Ja, ack,* this room, this room. Ingrid had sighed in her rememberings. How the silences spoke of the life which once flowed within these walls, within this old log house, this landmark along the wild, forested shores of the Great Lake.

* * *

In recalling her visit to the old home that evening and listening again to the various themes of the past, Ingrid also recalled the strong compulsion which had come over her as dusk had begun to fall on the strange day. She wondered how she might breathe a bit of life into the forsaken dwelling, if only for a moment of time. How could she lift the spell of death, emptiness, desolation? How could she set the old home breathing, stirring, opening its eyes once more? Oh, for a beam of light coming from its window once more as it did in the past when night drew on!

She recalled her search for a kerosene lamp. Climbing the stairs to the little room under the eaves, she found the lamp that had once shed its light on her father's Swedish Bible as he had sat beside his home-made desk, late in the evening, seeking a needed promise from its pages. The lamp still held some drops of oil. Ingrid carried it down the narrow, creaking stairway, trimmed the wick, and touched it with the flame of a match. Then she set the lighted lamp beside the window facing the path which led to the other neighbor.

Stepping out into the descending night, she walked to the gate which had once opened to the intriguing trail. Looking back, she beheld the miracle. A light in the window—once again! Even more amazing was this light tonight than she remembered from early years, tramping home from town after dark. How the light in the window spoke of life, direction, comfort, security. How this lighted window had once meant rescue and fresh courage to the sailor engulfed in a sea of billows! How it had dispelled bleakness and lostness to the foot-weary stranger and promised hope for the night—a place where he might lay his head. And what comfort the beams from this window gave to the only neighbor as he looked out upon the dark at bedtime. A lamp-lit window. Ingrid gazed with intense absorption. It was as if a bright star had suddenly appeared in a sky that had long been star-less.

Just a light in the window, and again the years had rolled back like a scroll, beyond the time of her father's death, to the days when family life had been young and whole. She saw her mother moving about preparing the evening meal. She saw her brothers coming in for the night, one carrying an armload of wood, another a pail of water from the lake. There was George coming from his traps, a muskrat dangling by his side. It had all seemed so real. Above the old pine the evening star shone as before. It had never changed. The moon was still gathering material for a golden bridge across the wide waters. It, too, had never changed.

*   *   *

She saw her oldest brother, Anders, coming from the barn carrying in the heavy pails of milk. *Ja*, Anders. How well she remembered his selfless boyhood, the surrender of his own early dreams in order to keep the farm alive. When his father's health and strength had begun to decline, it was Anders who set his young hands to the plow, his formal education ending before he had finished grammar school. There was no choice but to turn his ambition from school books to the raw soil. This he had done with no outward show of disappointment, even though he may have done some deep thinking. In the school room he may have dreamed of preparing himself for a less strenuous future. Some tears may have dropped on the old plow as he followed its furrow—wondering.

He began early to learn the language of the field and the upturned sod. His ear became sensitive to the heart-throb in the meadowlark's song. He drew from the earth beneath his feet nourishment for mind, body, and soul. As a tree strikes roots in a soil it may not have chosen and begins to grow, to put forth branches beautiful with blossom, rich with fruit, so Anders related himself to his environment and grew in strength and inner stature until his life branched out into many forms of usefulness and blessing to his family as well as to the community in which he was destined to live and serve.

Deep within him were aspirations, hungers, talents.

107

What he had learned in the brief years at school he had carefully preserved. His natural love for literature revealed itself in the poems he had memorized. Many were the evenings when a familiar group of friends, gathered around a beach fire, would call on Anders to recite one of his favorite poems. There was dignity in his appearance as he rose from his driftwood log to speak. Would it be Longfellow's *Skeleton in Armor*, *The Barefoot Boy* by Whittier, or some other choice revelation of human life born in the master heart of a famous poet?

There was depth in his face and fervor in his voice as he began, and his listeners were ready for flight into other worlds, worlds of peace or struggle, depending on his selection.

> *Speak! speak! thou fearful guest*
> *Who with thy hollowed breast*
> *Still in rude armor dressed,*
> *Comest to daunt me!*
>
> *Wrapped not in Eastern balms,*
> *But with thy fleshless palms*
> *Stretched, as if asking alms,*
> *Why dost thou haunt me?*

*Ja*, that was Anders.

His sensitivity to the meadowlark's song never left him. His quality of perception showed up in all his work. As he grew in years, his creative nature found outlets in various ways, not least in his skill at woodworking. Ingrid had heard of the beautiful altar setting in the Lutheran church which gave evidence of his artistic talent as well as craftmanship.

There were others in the community along the

shores whose names, also, are listed among the silent great.

❀    ❀    ❀

Ingrid remembered leaving her place at the gate to search for some trace of the old path which had wound in such exciting ways between the two neighbors. But there seemed to be no familiar sign left of the foot path through the leafy forest. She looked to the tall firs hiding the view of the lake, still serving as a windbreak. *Ja, ack,* if this wasn't the place where their first horse, Walter, had been buried. Somewhere near the feet of these pines had been the mound where he slept in death. Walter, the horse.

It was a sad day when Walter left. Even her father had shed tears as he dug the grave for his much-needed helpmate a few feet in from the path. For several years Ingrid and the other children conducted services beside his grave. It soon became a cemetery for dead birds and other pets of the wilderness. Wild flowers were faithfully laid on the graves in the summer, and carefully chosen stones of granite picked from the shores served as markers on each mound. There had been tears as in innocency they sang what Swedish songs they knew beside the dead:

> *De samlas nu hem från varje land,*
> *En och en, en och en.*

Death was not a hushed, concealed note in the pioneer drama of childhood. Death was real. The Holy City on the other side of the stormy sea was no fantasy. But to the child it was difficult to believe that there was no eternal future for the faithful horse

109

and the innocent songbird. And thus they stood by
the graves and sang:

> *När kampen de slutat de hvilan nå*
> *En och en, en och en.*

Ingrid could still hear Isak's voice leading in the
refrain:

> *They gather now home from many lands*
> *One by one, one by one.*

It was a high moment of childhood, singing beside
the graves at the side of the path. *Ja,* that was then.

Darkness had settled over the shores when Ingrid
left the animal cemetery to feel her way back. She
wished she could have lingered in what had once
been the wild raspberry patch near one end of the
trail, but the years had now changed that area into a
barnyard with a large stable across the path from it.
Instead of raspberry bushes calling one on a hot summer day there were mooing cows, squawking hens,
and crowing roosters.

How often Ingrid had recalled this fragrant raspberry patch where the children met to refresh themselves. This was not the day when road stands
offering ice cream cones, cheerios, popsickles, and
pizzas were near at hand. But there had been a wild
raspberry patch! Here Ingrid and the other children
had found sweet refreshment when free from their
tasks on a hot summer day. How luscious had been
the taste, like an oasis in a thirsty land.

She remembered the August afternoons when the
two mothers and their children had met here with

pails, pans, and cups to gather berries to preserve as delicacies against the long winter days. How much fun it had been, especially when the afternoon sun began to turn westward over the Big Slough and you heard your neighbor Emma say:

"*Ja*, come now, we will go into my house for a good cup of coffee. All of you."

It was a cozy, shady path which led right up to Emma's kitchen door. It was arbored with birches and poplars. A child's swing hung invitingly between two tall trees, suggesting a moment's pause. Ingrid remembered the certain thrill that came as they walked this narrow lane to the door of the other home. To old and young Emma's kitchen had the fragrance of happiness in it. How many times they had feasted at her large kitchen table with food surprises such as few other pantries had in store. *Ack*, it was fun. But that was long ago, and youth was no more.

As the child in Ingrid went away, she remembered footing her way back from the memories of the raspberry patch and Emma's kitchen to the old homestead where the lamp in the window was still sending its flow of light into the dark—the light that had for a brief hour lifted the empty shell out of its depression. Now she must prayerfully extinguish the little flame and turn her back upon a dwelling that must once more return to darkness and desolation, its heartbeat silenced. If the closing chapter of its history was now nearing the end, she would always remember the lighted window as a beautiful and appropriate amen.

Years have passed since that strange visit to the scenes of her childhood. Now, in the twilight of her life, she would return and set foot once more on the hallowed ground. *Ja,* tomorrow she would go back. What would she find tomorrow?

## 12. HOME AGAIN

Then came the morning of that other day—tomorrow. Ingrid awakened to find that overnight nature had changed its garments of sackcloth and ashes into a robe of sinless white. The waves on the Great Lake were no longer pounding the shores. Like children exhausted from healthy play, they were ready to go to sleep.

Ingrid knew from experience that in this northland of hers November was not likely to forget to introduce the first snowfall. Some time during the night the silent heaven had let fall from its vast sieve a light shower of feathery flakes, and in the midst of the white silence footsteps of approaching winter could be heard. The trees, stripped to their naked bodies, were moist with white fluff, their shrouded limbs adding an atmosphere of heavenly peace to the new day. And in this spell of wonder Ingrid set out for the old homestead down on the shores. She wondered what she would find when she visited it this time. What transformation could have taken place since last she saw it?

*Ja*, the old homestead. She recalled the time when she and her brothers saw no hope for the place but to sell it. There seemed no reason for holding on to the sagging house with its deteriorating field and orchard. It had served its day. In fact, the outlook for the little settlement bordering the lake was not a promising one. Farms lay idle, and the lumber and logging industry was a thing of the yesteryears. Thus for a meager sum the little home and its surroundings went into the hands of another owner. In the years that followed it was sold twice more, its desolation deepening with each year until the fourth owner, a doctor from the southern part of the state, saw what no one else had seen, the hidden possibilities of this lakeside property and the surrounding countryside.

How did it happen that the new buyer came all the way to the front porch of Wisconsin to inquire about this neglected homestead? What charm did it possess that awakened his interest?

The secret lay hidden in a book he had come across. A book may have the power to open windows that look out upon the daybreak of coming eras. Sitting up late one night, his interest had increased with each chapter. Here was enchantment! It described a piece of God's creation nestled along the shore of the Great Lake and told of the unique experience of two Swedish families who ventured into this rugged wilderness with nothing but a will to work and a firm faith in God. Here was drama! The very title of the book revealed the philosophy by which they lived: *Comes the Day, Comes a Way.* By the time he had finished the last chapter he had caught a vision—a dream had been born, a resolve made.

For many weeks the book lay open on his desk while he made inquiries and plans concerning this alluring lakeside property.

"Something is calling me," he said. "I must get up to this place." Here was a story that must not end. It called for continuance, a sequel in which he must have a part.

When he was informed that the old homestead was again in search of a new owner, he was not slow in making his way northward. In a short time papers were drawn up, and the little log dwelling with its surrounding land became his. Thus began a new chapter in the story of the old homestead.

It was midmorning the day when Ingrid entered the narrowing forest lane which had once been the main road to the Isakson and Hanson lakeshore farms. It was good to travel back to childhood, to yesterday, to the place of dreams—and home.

*Ja,* think—home. As she came within sight of the old dwelling, the sun came out and flooded the day with new outlook. When an unexpected sun appears and smiles over a world of white, there is paradise for you.

As she approached the old home, her attention

was immediately called to a signboard across the upper front wall, just below the peak of the roof. Something leaped inside her. Here were the words which formed the title of the book the doctor had been reading: *"Comes the Day, Comes a Way."* She paused for a moment in speechless wonder, her eyes fixed on nothing else but the sign—the title of her own book written several years before. Could it be that something about this place still belonged to her in a deeper way than she had dreamed?

One surprise followed another as she looked around the place. She missed the north wing, which had been severed from the rest of the building. This was the addition, made of lumber, which had been added years after the original cabin had been built. Ingrid remembered her elation when she returned home from her school in the city one summer to find how her father had enlarged the old home and covered the logs with siding and a coat of paint.

*Ja,* a new house! It was everyone's dream to outgrow the old log shell and build a new home in more modern style with lumber instead of rough logs. It was a mark of progress.

Ingrid could still see broken blocks of stone scattered around the spot on which her father had planned to lay the foundation for a new home. *Ja, ack,* dreams do not always come true. When Ingrid's father realized that he would never have the means or the strength to build a new home, he chose to do the next best. His broken dreams resulted in this small addition on the north side of the old log house, with siding covering the whole cabin and a cheerful, yellow coat of paint. *Ja,* think, poverty can blast many a dream, but it can also awaken creativity. The

116

old home had shone in splendor as it rose close to the side of the blue waters. *Ja,* that was then.

Ingrid looked around the place. Not only had the north wing been severed from the rest of the house, but all the siding had been ripped off. The old log house of the early 90's was back to its genesis of naked logs. What was more, it had been moved fifty feet to the east of its original setting, affording it shelter against a background of younger pines and spruces.

Inside, endless hours of scrubbing and scraping had restored the beauty of pine floors worn smooth by countless footsteps of the past. The walls which had stood speechless and cold for the intervening years were now warm and alive. Fresh chinking and plastering between the logs had replaced the moss filling which had been there since the log house was built.

Leaving the house, Ingrid was glad to see the old mountain ash by which her mother had often sat drinking her midmorning coffee. How she delighted in these forenoon breaks in the shade of the ash or on a driftwood log beside the chattering waters. *"Ombyte förnyas,"* she would say whenever she stole a moment to do something different—"A change makes things new."

Ingrid remembered the washday morning when Mama, tired of carrying pails of water from the lake to the house, decided to try a new method for rinsing. She carried the basket of handscrubbed laundry down to the lake and threw the whole batch, from socks to sheets, into its swirling waters. Later when her neighbor Emma happened to come by, Mama was standing knee-deep in the lake rinsing her

117

cottons, calicos, and jerseys, then tossing them on a log raft near shore. "*Ja,* Emma, you have no more fun than you make for yourself." Emma smiled. She knew Mama's genius for new ways of doing things.

Behind the house and almost hidden by the firs Ingrid discovered a pile of rough lumber. Inquiring about its purpose, she was told that the new owner was planning to re-enact a chapter from *Comes the Day* titled "The Fisherman's Cottage." Her father had once built such a cottage along the shore for company—visiting pastors and their families, fishermen, or anyone in need of a temporary home. The Fisherman's Cottage was an interesting addition to the lake shore. Again Ingrid experienced a strange flood of exaltation. Could it be that she shared the old home in a way she had never known before? *Ja, ack,* here was evidence of the yesterdays come to life again, a dream coming into fruition, with creative planning and careful labor to bring the old dwelling out of its depression into the atmosphere and appearance of its original setting. Dr. K., the owner, had captured the philosophy of the early settler and again given reality to the Swedish proverb: "Comes the day, comes a way." Yesterday and today were shaking hands.

After having explored the old home and its surroundings, Ingrid decided to go in search of a landmark deeply set in the history of childhood. She started for the field, passing the place where the old barn had once stood. In early years the field behind it was but a small clearing, the upper end of which was edged by a grove of saplings. It was in this woodland of wild cherry, poplar, and birch that the first grave had been dug.

The mind will forget many things and yet hold on to some single event buried deep in the heart. Though nearly seventy-five years had passed, this memory had not lost its grip. How well she remembered that Sunday afternoon back in the years—the little mound and the wooden pillar which served as a marker. She could still feel the hush of the green grove and inhale the fragrance of wild cherry bloom. How often she had walked the slender trail which led to the grave, carrying a handful of wild daisies or roses to place on the little mound. The place had become an altar, a place of childhood worship where the songs she had learned were sung and holy reverence was expressed in audible prayer.

But what had become of the little grave? Ingrid had often looked for a sign of the exact location. The grove of trees had disappeared as the early clearing had expanded into a larger field, and the little knoll had sunk into the flat of the meadow. No longer did a gray marker point heavenward. *Ja, ack.* This was often the fate of the first graves in the pioneering days. With no public cemetery, graves were dug here and there—in the field, along the road, or in the deep woods.

Today a state highway crosses the field very close to baby Ruth's grave. Who knows how close, wondered Ingrid. And the speed of another age rushes across the sober silence of a yesterday.

Ingrid still remembered the little group that stood around the grave that long-ago Sunday afternoon. She recalled the songs they sang about the land across the stormy Jordan. She remembered the closing words of the service when the simple coffin, which her father had made, was lowered. "Ashes to

119

ashes, dust to dust." *Ja*, that is what had happened. Dust. It is the interlude between the time of sleep and the great awakening. But the memory does not go to dust.

In serious thought Ingrid turned from the field where baby Ruth's grave was hidden and set off for the lake shore, still searching for landmarks associated with childhood. *Ja, ack*, there was the old pine, still in its place near the lake. Its infancy dated back to the days when the red man canoed the Gitche Gume waters. It was still towering skyward. She tried to put her arms around its trunk as she had done as a child but could not circle its rugged body anymore. Standing in the path of the northwesterlies, it had sheltered the little home by taking the first full buffetings of the wind, thus easing the force of the gusts as they slapped against the house. "There is heroism," her father had said. *Ja*, that was then.

As Ingrid reached the lake shore, she was reminded of the many happy summer days she and the other children had enjoyed here. By now the sun had melted away the snow on the deep, rich sands in which the creative arts of childhood had once found full play. It was in these moist sands that little homes were molded, farmsteads shaped into being, and even little villages—like the town that was going up a few miles from the Hanson and Isakson farms. There was the large mill, a store, a street with little homes in a row. But how transient were the sand villages along the lake. Overnight they could be washed away by the waves of the lake. "It is the way of earth," her father would say. The experience was a sermon for future years to interpret.

Earth was not the goal of the early Christian

settlers. They considered themselves but pilgrims and sojourners here. There was a purpose for being here which affected both time and eternity. Many of their edifices have been washed away by the billows of time, but something intangible lives on, instilling in others faith and appreciation for matters that lie beyond the realm of earth. Their simple, childlike trust in God and His Word and the influence of their prayers are still at work. While they sojourned here, they gave witness to it, they sang it, they worked for it. The urgency of their prayers for the growing generation could be read in the deep furrows of their faces. And from these shores have come great lives dedicated to the service of God and man. Not all seeds that were planted in those long-ago years fell by the wayside. Many grew into beautiful Christian fruitage.

* * *

Sunset and evening star. A gentle south wind whistled an evening melody across the grasses of the Big Slough, and Ingrid knew that as evening wore on the melodies of night would have full play. It was the time of day when heaven in breathless wonder declares the culmination of another day. Endings can be beautiful. It may be the crimson skyline laying its benediction upon a completed day or the consummation of a great truth in the closing stanza of a heaven-born poem. In the cadence of a song the soul finds its loftiest flight as the last tones taper into time. Endings may open doors to the world beyond.

And now twilight was beginning to settle across the land and sea. Ingrid was aware that someone would be coming to bring her back to town. This would be her last visit on the homestead shores.

121

Tomorrow she would return to the city. She must make the most of these ending moments. Here by the listening post beside the water's edge she had stood as a young child, hearkening to the questions which came from the heart of the Great Lake—"Who are you?" "From where did you come?" "Where are you going?" A child leaning close to the breast of nature may hear what the ears of middle life may never hear. In the full-packed intermediate years when life spins at high momentum one does not always take time to hearken to the divine overtones that are all around. But now, having reached the evening years of life, Ingrid found that the gift of hearing had returned in a deep, meaningful way. The words of the prophet Isaiah came to her remembrance: "He wakeneth mine ear to hear."

As she listened, she seemed to hear voices coming from another world—from a city not built on the perishable sands of earth. They were singing again—Hogberg, Guldstrand, Johanna, Emma, and many others—these early settlers who in faith once tramped the raw, unknown wilderness along the shores of the Great Lake. It was the song that had often rung through the forest aisles when they gathered for worship in God's outdoor cathedral. Conscious of their many shortcomings and transgressions and aware of the depth of forgiveness that only Christ can give, they had sung the song with quiverings in their voices.

*Ja,* that was then. But this night, listening from the water's edge, Ingrid heard a triumphant fervor in their song:

> *Only a sinner*
> *Saved by grace.*

122

*"Frälst av nåd."* Over and again she heard the flow of the three closing notes: "Saved by grace." Endings can hold wonder.

The night was studded in glowing starlight when Ingrid turned from the high moment on the shores. She would hold the cadence of this last day in her heart forever.

# Glossary

124

*Oss en källa har Gud beredt,*
*En källa öppen och fri.*

*Tänkespråk*

God has prepared for us a spring,
A spring open and free.

Memory verse

*Men nu förbliva tro, hopp,*
*kärlek, dessa tre, men störst*
*ibland dem är kärlek.*

Now abideth faith, hope, love, these
three; but the greatest of these is
love.

*Ja, visst*

Certainly

*Jag kände evigheten där uppe.*
*Blott en dag, ett ögonblick i sänder,*

*Vilken tröst, evad som kommer på!*
*Allt ju vilar i min Faders händer,*
*Skulle jag, som barn, väl ängslas då?*

I felt eternity up there.
Day by day, and with each passing
moment,
Strength I find to meet my trials here;
Trusting in my Father's wise bestowment,
I've no cause for worry or for fear.

*Julotta*

Early morning service on Christmas Day

*Var hälsad, sköna morgonstund,*
*Som av profeters helga mun*
*Är oss bebådad vorden!*
*Du stora dag, du sälla dag,*
*På vilken himlens välbehag*
*Ännu besöker jorden!*

All hail to thee, O blessed morn!
To tidings, long by prophets borne,
Hast Thou fulfillment given.
O sacred and immortal day,
When unto earth, in glorious ray,
Descends the grace of heaven!

*Herrens nåd är var morgon ny.*
*Varför skulle vi sörja?*
*Jordens skuggor, hur snart de fly,*
*Må var lovsång då börja.*

God's grace is new each morning.
Why should we be sad?
Earth's shadows, how soon they pass,
Let our song of praise begin.

*De samlas nu hem från varje land,*
*En och en, en och en.*

They are gathered home from every land,
One by one, one by one.

*När kampen de slutat de hvilan nå,*

*En och en, en och en.*

When the struggle is over, they reach
their rest,
One by one, one by one.

*Ombyte förnyas*

A change makes things new.

125